Made In Kenya

Made In Kenya

FEISAL NANJI

ISBN: 0990966607
ISBN 13: 9780990966609
Library of Congress Control Number: 2014921545
Absurd Humor Publishing, New York, NY

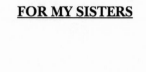

FOR MY SISTERS

Authors Note:

*T*he events in this book may or may not have occurred. Treat it as a work of fiction.

Preface: Not All Fun and Games

Roaming street urchins were a sad fact of Nairobi life. I didn't know if they were orphans, or if they had left their slums and struggling mothers for the day to steal, find some fun, adventure or food. Many were tots, about six or seven. They had dirty, tear-streaked faces and all were barefoot, dressed in rags or remnants of clothes that simply could not be repaired; bums often showing through the rips.

And there I was, avoiding eye contact with these boys who could have easily been me. I probably smelled like Pears soap after Mummy had forced me to take a nice hot shower. My hair would be washed, combed and parted to portray the good little boy that I was and my teeth cleaned courtesy of Colgate. I would not be wearing flashy clothes, but my shirt would have been of good quality, perhaps bought at Deacons on Kimathi Street, which sold the very English Marks and Spencer brand. To shuffle around in my privilege I likely also had a pair of dependable Clarks on my feet. And of course I would be headed to the movies, walking to the 20th Century cinema to see a comedy such as a *Mad, Mad World*.

It made no sense to me. And still doesn't. How can it, when one sees a boy barely eight use his lightning quick reflexes to nab a slow pigeon, rip it apart and bite into its raw flesh? This hunger and sadness was a constant of life in Africa. It wasn't sushi at Nobu. For anyone who has lived in Africa, Asia or Latin America, this is a suffering we ignore to make it through every day.

One afternoon I was walking past the Kenya Commercial Bank head-quarters with a meat pie from Sussex Bakery in my hand. I had made a special trip to the far side of town, to get the delicious, light, perfectly crusted snack when two large Alsatians (German shepherds) held tight by the bank sentries, smelled the meat. Both animals rose up on their hind legs and began barking, seething and wanting, it seemed, to devour not just my snack but me as well. The dogs' handlers reined them in and I was safe, for now. From the corner of my eye, next to one of the classical Greek columns supporting the bank, I saw a bedraggled urchin witnessing the proceedings. He ran toward me sensing an opportunity. No more than six, he brazenly snatched the pie out my hand, escaped and wolfed it down. The little boy was hungrier than the dogs. When I recounted this event to Mummy, she said, as only a Saint could, "Don't worry. The boy was not to blame. He just wanted food. Think of it as a gift to him, and not a theft."

We don't know who to blame for these ills or who to thank for those of us blessed with luck. It can't be God, can it? God is merciful, God is great! If so, where is he?

This little set of vignettes of my life ignores the stark reality of Africa's destitution, of the real Africa that seethed and cried out for help near the manicured lawns of Nairobi School and the safety of our Indian communities. Perhaps when the *Singularity is Near*, we will be rid of this pain, and I can write more fully about my home.

Highridge Flats

I could hear his breathing. Twilight on Africa's Equator is over in a flash and I had little time before it turned solidly dark. As I approached the gate like a stealthy big cat, his mad bark went off. In the shroud of the completing darkness I saw the angry glint of teeth and his furious attempts to jump over and kill me with rabies or the sheer power of his jaws.

I was late coming home from the Club and I had to pay my penance. The dog's name was Fido and he belonged to Kuljeet's family who lived in a small bungalow covered in dense green. It seemed to me that Fido had inherited his traits from Kuljeet who was a bully, sadist, and at 13, was a year older than me. The dog had been trained to bark incessantly at any movement by black skin. When dark happened, we argued if the dog could tell the difference between brown and black. It was a topic that often came up as we sat on the middle field steps telling ghost stories or recalling scenes from our favorite movie, *The Exorcist*.

"Dogs don't have X-Ray vision," Khanbhai cried.

"What do you know? Dogs can see better in the dark," Lalji said.

Virani said the obvious on everyone's mind, "That Singho hates us. I wish he would die."

"Someone should hang him by his turban," Minu said, and everyone snickered.

"Then all the dudus from his pagri would spill out and we would have cholera," Khanbhai pointed out, and with that the small group of us boys erupted into unbridled laughter. We were home and safe in our gated Ismaili compound, guarded by two Askaris or sentries at each entrance. We could afford to be brave.

To us it was a recurring, funny slur to speak of Sikhs carrying colonies of insects in their turbans. What else could it be? Anyway the image of red ants or senenes making a home in a human's head was packed with humor. Of course one could never say that to a Sikh's face. The turbaned chap would be inevitably stronger than you, and definitely crazier. Angering a Sikh meant he was likely to rip you into shreds, if not beat the crap out of you with his ever-present hockey stick.

In Kenya, the Sikhs were the undisputed masters of hockey, sending teams of young turbaned men to play for the illustrious Kenyan team. We even won the Bronze medal in the Olympics once and without the Sikhs we could not have even gotten on the plane. Many years later, while watching *Star Trek: The Next Generation*, a mystery of the universe was revealed to me when I realized that the Klingons and Sikhs had shared genes.

Besides their affinity for hockey and rabid dogs, the Sikhs also played some strange devotional music at about four PM. Each day, on the way back from our primary school at the corner of Mumtaz Road and 5th Parklands Avenue, we heard the thump of tablas and infrequent high-pitched wails as we passed the large Sikh house named *Dogra Nivas*. Over time, we even began to enjoy the precise, resonant beats if not the high pitch. But why someone would want to name a house the "House of Smells" we couldn't fathom. That Dogra Nivas was the literal translation in Gujarati, and not the language of Punjabi, which the Sikhs spoke, was of little concern to us. Didn't the turban-wallahs have enough sense? It seemed they almost enjoyed being ridiculed.

Our middle-field, where we exchanged the merits of life and laughter was exactly that; a slightly sloping patch of Kikuyu grass encircled by our townhomes or flats. It served as our playing field and hosted soccer games, a slightly sunken marble pitch, and hockey matches. Appropriately placed light poles, served as goalposts and to string badminton nets. This particular spot in the field was dotted with white feathers that fell off the shuttlecocks from the incessant swishing of rackets.

Middle-field also had room for a small cricket pitch. For this it was truly magical. Several bumps by the creases helped us practice against future foes at school who might throw off-spinners, leg breaks or even the mighty googly. Because the batting end of the pitch was lower than the crease from where one bowled, we could also imitate our Australian pace-bowler heroes Dennis Lillee and Jeff Thompson. We would play cricket with a tennis ball, or, when we had gumption and the feeling of invincibility, a hard ball.

As kids, middle–field was our beloved playground. Ensconced by a circle of flats including my parents' own, rarely were we subject to taunting from someone who lived outside our compound. As we matured into pimply-faced teenagers with deeper voices, we would sit on the steps that led from middle-field to a smidgen of more grass and eventually to the footpath toward my house. At this throne where we held court, the world's ponderous questions would be solved with the ease of Minaz Charania's bombast or from my own encyclopedic knowledge stolen from the shining set of Britannica in our front room. I was somewhat of a know-it-all, but I also made up a lot of stuff which, while plausible, always had a fundamental weakness that quickly rendered my opinions inconsequential.

Moreover, in a group of 12 to 15 year olds, it wasn't how you thought, but what you looked like or how you played the game. Muscles mattered. Skinny as a rake, my biceps and especially my long anemic legs, did not garner much respect. I wasn't a dazzling centre-forward, or a fast runner.

In fact, my very slowness often made me the last pick in hockey and foot-ball. I minded a lot, but with the constant attention of the best mother in the world, I had little to worry about. She was always there to salve any hurt or ignominy with the ease of a master masseuse. Mummy knew what it meant to be hurt but she had a built in mechanism for letting it slide off her shoulders and disappear in the focus of what really mat-tered. She laughed at my jokes, shielded me from the barbs that Papa so accurately aimed at me, and made sure that my sister, Ferry, always had a nice new dress for an important religious festival.

I tried many sports to become a worthy boy. Over the years, I dras-tically improved my hand-eye coordination by hitting a ping-pong ball mercilessly against the wall in our tiny sitting room with my trusty Chinese-made "Double Happiness" bat. I eventually became good enough to enter several table tennis tournaments during adolescence. The best I ever did was to reach the semi-finals of our local club tourna-ment. While there wasn't a trophy for losing the semi-finals, there was, however, a trophy for the "best performance" – or best upset. This, I won after beating the number two seed in straight sets. It was one of the proudest moments of my sporting career. I placed the trophy next to one of Papa's. It looked a bit silly for it was small and one couldn't discern my prize from the 50 or so my father had won as a tennis maven. But it was mine, and it still reigns as the major accomplishment of my highly varied sporting career.

I wanted to be a football star, tennis professional, a black belt in karate, and an awesome cricketer. This lack of focus, of course didn't serve me well. I quit karate after realizing that punches do hurt. I gave up football and playing goalkeeper after getting my spectacles broken by a mighty boot that left a crease on the bridge of my nose. There were so many other simple reasons why I didn't excel other sports. But I did rela-tively well in cricket. Through the fortunate attrition of fellow African boys disinterested in playing a silly game only Indians and white folk played, our high school team struggled to field a decent side. But exactly because of this pleasant circumstance I managed to walk on to our high school's First Eleven. We played ten matches that year losing seven and drawing three. But, oh how sweet were the ties!

It was at middle-field where I honed my cricket skills. I was an accurate bowler. And, with what I thought was flawless form, I was able to hurl the rock at pace that belied my skinny strength. This, and my ability to react quickly to sharply hit balls, boosted my status among the boys. As luck would have it, not being a complete flake in cricket allowed me to not be embarrassed for being born a boy.

Hair

On my twelfth birthday Mummy bought me some long pants after realizing that other boys my age were not showing off the knotty hair that covered their thighs. Many of us Indian boys, including myself, were hirsute. Our heads were full of hair – mostly straight, but sometimes curly, and mostly always dark-jet black hair. One of my pals since I was five, Adil Gilani, had a shock of lustrous brown hair of the like we saw in the commercials for Vo5 hair spray. I don't know whose genes were in the pudding when he was made, but with his very fair skin and his splendorous mop, he was the darling of older girls aged fourteen or so who were coming into their own beauty. This made me quite jealous, for I wasn't the one being fawned over.

So I decided to undergo a makeover. Getting Mummy to buy me long pants was the first step. She got a bargain at River Road, the Mecca of Nairobi's discount stores, and she bought me two pairs. I tried them on immediately. They were a bit short, but if I pulled down on them to sit slightly below the waist, they were passable. The next improvement was my hair. I'd work on Mummy for new, more fashionable glasses later. I was a good boy and realized that Mummy had a tight budget – I only asked for things when absolutely necessary, which was after all the other boys in the flats, had got theirs. Whether this was a pair of trousers, or a new bicycle or a board game like Monopoly, I didn't ask for these items until the pain of envy would reveal itself in a young boy's pleading.

The next step I took to being a boy hunk was to fix my hair. I couldn't show off my muscles, because I didn't have any, my teeth were average, and I didn't have enough hair on my face to shave. I could try and use my father shaving brush and razor to remove the barely visible soft moustache, but the time was not now. I had heard if you shaved too early, your balls would shrink, or your voice would never break and remain forever in its childish high pitch. So shaving, at this point, was simply too risky.

What I could do however, was get fliccups, like Bashir (Bash) who lived up from the middle field in flat # 80. (There were 93 flats in total in our compound – 93 families of various sorts, but all Ismaili, and, for the most part respectable.). Bash was several years older than me and was my hero. His hair was long at the back and it curled into a highly fashionable thing us kids called "fliccups". Apparently, some big singers had these. I might have even seen a picture of one of those "Beetles" have one.

Bash also wore thick glasses and had a pleasant air about him. Two sisters who lived near his house, Shan and Shenny, liked his jokes, and Shan, as the prettiest girl in the flats, lent him a shiny aura. Getting someone as pretty as Shan to like me would send me to the moon. I couldn't possibly expect that level of girl to fall in love with me for the rest of my life; I knew my looks weren't that good. But if a girl with even half of Shan's beauty were to take any interest in me I would be king. So my model was Bashir. I would conquer women with wit and humor, my own set of thick spectacles, and a humongous fliccup that would curl up like Samantha's in *Bewitched*.

Getting a fliccup, however, was not a simple task, especially for someone whose hair was as straight as a slide rule. This required a bit of hair training, so after my nightly shower, I would take a couple of hair pins, twist my wet hair at the back into two separate rolls, and hold them up with the pins. My thinking was that once the hair dried it would "set" into a curl. After all, many of the ladies in the flats had Saturday appointments at hairdressers to "set" their hair. I convinced myself that if performed diligently, this nightly ritual would lead to the much desired curl.

My fliccup development could not be called a major success. I did manage to get the inklings of a curl, and I would use a comb when my hair was dry to coax the curl to stay. I bought a new comb for this – a brand new "Semperit" that was small enough to fit neatly into my pocket. All the older guys had combs, so this added to my self-worth. Now that my tiny curl was in place, I had to crane my neck or twist it like a cockatoo to show off its vast beauty. Reflecting back, I must have looked like a spastic whenever a girl passed by. (See my fliccup! Am I not so handsome? What? You didn't see it? Then what about the other side? Please don't go away without acknowledging the sheer art that is my hair!)

Then one day Shenaz Virjee, one of older sister Ferry's good pals came up to me. Shenaz was a pretty young thing with long legs, but a bit couth for my taste since she knew she was a hottie and flaunted it. She looked hard at me as if to examine for blackheads or give my beloved curl a deep second look. Gee whiz, my face flushed. I *was* going on to be anointed as a handsome devil. But instead of warm sounds, she said, "You know what Feshu; your ears are really big." Not a single word on the splendor of my hair. "They are like Big Ears' in the Noddy books," she said.

Noddy books were authored by that wondrous, Enid Blyton, who wrote superlatively for children of many ages. In the Noddy series, Big Ears was an elderly elf who was attentive to and patient with a rambunctious Noddy. While he was endearing, Big Ears sported embarrassingly large ears that stuck out like happy cauliflowers.

To me, getting another slight added to my long list that included "skinny balunki" and "microscope glasses" because of my thick specs was enough to shatter my illusions. The fliccups alone would not be worthy of teen-girl adulation. Not wanting to give up hope I embarked on yet another self-beautification project.

Yes my ears were large, but that wasn't the problem. The cause of concern was that they stuck out like darts, overwhelming my round baby face and humiliating my latent good looks. Shenaz was right and this physical defect had to be addressed forcefully. So over the next few weeks I slept with a tight hair band that kept my ears pressed to the side of the head. I would look at the mirror every few days trying to find any progress. When this visual evidence was not conclusive, I resorted to a trusty foot ruler to get a more precise estimate. But these measurements too were filled with error. Intuitively I knew that my experiment might be a failure. So without any definitive results, I resigned myself to a life without girls. It was a sad moment of truth, but as a romantic 12 year old I had to face up to this stark reality.

And yet a world devoid of girls was not the final insult in my self-makeover. That last zinger came at the hands of a doddering, cranky septuagenarian. Prayers at the mosque started at 6:30 pm, just about the time when the sun went to spend the night behind a stand of stately Jacaranda trees. My cousin Aleem and I were trying to make it in time before the prayers started. Coming in late to mosque was frowned upon by the fascist elders who pointed out that tardiness was a clear sign of ingrained rebellion or heresy. Aleem, of course, the world's number 1 boy in the eyes of the adults in my orbit, had convinced me with his usual charm to make the walk between our flats and the mosque in a scant 12 minutes and not the usual 17. This was a fast pace, and attainable without running, but there should be no impediments or diversions along the way.

Fido, Kuljeet Singh's mad dog, could not be baited, and a new survey to see what lay behind the secretive Ismail-Karsanji's opaque gate could not deter us. It wasn't that I was devoted follower, but I had to pretend to be one. Aleem, after all, was the best student in School, annoyingly devout, a terrific swimmer, had fair skin, and a lovely mother (my aunt

9

Sultan) who made scrumptious silver dollar pancakes. If I was to be compared to him, as I always was, the least I could do was try and be second best. Being on time for mosque by putting in an extra effort would be lauded if noticed and might earn me an imaginary silver star. Lord knows, I needed so many of these just to avoid golden boy Aleem leaving me in a cloud of his magic do-gooder dust.

In nine quick minutes we were at the gates of a large compound across our primary school. These 50 acres or so housed the mosque, our sporting club's cricket and football pitch, a badminton hall, two tennis courts and plenty of parking. The mosque was only 100 yards away from the main gates giving us plenty of time to break the 12 minute barrier we had allotted our selves. Or so I thought.

As we crossed the gates we heard a shrill voice, "Chokra (little boy)". We turned around to find an incensed old lady also making her way to the mosque. Paying respect to our elders (and especially the quite elderly), was a mantra drilled into us. When an adult called, one went meekly. When a really old person called you almost went in supplication.

What was the fuss about? Didn't the old crone know that prayers began at 6:30 sharp? We only had three minutes to get inside, remove and stow away our shoes before the call to prayer was sounded.

We stopped in front of her. In Gujarati, she addressed me and asked if I was trying to be a girl. Ah, this crinkle of a woman wasn't murderously angry. She was simply having fun at our expense. But wait, she wasn't joking, her black beady eyes held me at attention.

"Girl? No, I am not a girl," I said in what must have sounded like sotto voce.

Grabbing my beloved, fledgling fliccup, the granny pulled at my hair and said in Gujarati, "You need a ribbon for this. And only girls wear ribbons. The next time I see you I want it cut off."

The pain of getting one's hair pulled, as wrestlers can surely attest, is not a pleasant experience. But the humiliation of an elder's public admonishment is enough to cause a minor heart attack. Aleem, of course with his closely cropped head was spared the humiliation, and could safely announce that if wasn't for Feshu's need for fashion, we would have been on time. My silver star was collapsing on me, sucking out all the victory that was rightfully mine. At school on Monday, everyone who mattered would hear from Aleem's soapbox that I had been accosted by a granny who called me a girl. To avoid this cheek-flushing embarrassment, I asked Papa to take me to the Hadjam (barber) the very next day. Papa happily obliged as he saw no use for long hair either.

Mummy, who knew what I was trying to do, said in a most loving tone, "Don't worry betha, you will soon be a handsome, bright young man. I know it."

What would we do without mothers?

Golden Boy

Aleem was *the* golden boy. Consistently, the best student of my cohort, he was everyone's favorite. Indian parents of all sizes and shapes placed great worth on education. So having Aleem in the family was like having Elvis in our midst. He was a megastar not only because of his hard work and brains, but also because he was so very devout. He could read and write in Gujarati by the age of ten which made him the youngest ever to read our sacred scriptures in the language they were written. This was a big deal then. As I told my sister Ferry years later, it was like reading Aristotle in the original Greek.

At 13, in our last year at Aga Khan Primary school, Aleem was appointed "Head Boy" by the teachers. This meant he was in charge of all student boy-prefects including myself. I was lucky to have made it to prefect, not because of my overbearing presence, gumption or ability to mete out discipline, but because I was reasonably good student.

Being a prefect was a powerful honor. We could report any kind of student violation to the headmistress, who used us like Nazi youth to maintain some kind of order of over 1000 shrieking boys and girls aged 5 to 13. Prefects controlled the school by enforcing rules that included no use of swear words, no fighting, unnecessary bullying or girl teasing, and adherence to the full school uniform – Khaki shorts for the boys, a white collared shirt, a green pullover and a red and green striped tie. Violators would be reported to our school principal, Mrs. Kassam, who had the discretion to cane serious offenders.

Caning using a thin bamboo stick was a form of corporal punishment meted out on tiny buttocks. It not only hurt but was a high form of embarrassment. Very serious violations such as a full-fledged fight could result in suspension, or worse the dreaded "expulsion." Using fear to control a horde of children worked well to keep school order. Most violations occurred in recess or lunch and as Head Boy, Aleem was in charge of reporting all violations to the principal. But first he had to determine of the violation was worthy of sending someone to the principal's office. Again, golden boy Aleem did not disappoint here. He was fair but firm and the students knew it and gave him much deserved respect. His partner, the Head Girl, was Shelnin Khan, a lovely beauty with fashionable fish-eye glass frames that made her look like a young Nana Mouskouri. Aleem and she were perfectly matched.

So, in summary, not only was Aleem the best student in school, adored by his parents and legions of elders, but he had a lovely babe to call his "Head-Girl". If you were 13 and a boy, you might have thought you had died and gone to heaven.

Yet, in my view this Aleem-adulation was unnecessarily excessive. Yes, he was the smartest, hardest working student, and yes he was a do-gooder and could knit socks and bake Swiss rolls, but what the heck did adults know about the real Aleem? I did.

I *knew* the true measure of the boy. As his cousin and peer, I was around him much of the time. He was the closest thing I had to a brother. Perhaps my misgivings were a bit of sour grapes – (OK, perhaps a lot), but there were quite a few chinks in Aleem's impenetrable armor. Boys our age, especially in the flats thought he was just plain weird. I can't blame them for that. Having achieved everything a good little boy could achieve in his little life, Aleem wasn't much fun to our motley little group of flat boys. Aleem couldn't crack jokes, was horribly awkward at ball games, badminton and impeccably polite. What good was all the education in the world if you had absolutely no hope, zero, nada, for becoming a world class footballer, cricketer or foul-mouthed cop that all girls inevitably fell in love with? At least, as boys who could kick or catch a fucking ball for God's sake, we had a shot at stardom in the football World Cup or to play cricket for our club eleven. Where was the glory in becoming a great doctor or engineer, a promise that was Aleem's to pick for the choosing?

His academic talent ended up being the only thing he could rely on. Since so many of the flat boys were in awe of his academic accomplishments, he wasn't invited to share our secret hiding spots, or our frequent reconnaissance trips to spot a girls bare bum or bra strap. In brief, Aleem was a pariah of sorts to other flat boys and, unfortunately for Aleem, he knew that.

Being my closest boy relation however, I couldn't ignore him. In fact I liked him. We had much fun over the years, but his superiority at almost everything was annoying. So I had this love-hate relationship with him. This was exacerbated because he was a bit of a sadist to me. Underneath all the correctness, Aleem had a very, very mean streak. And all of this was aimed at me. I was an easy target of course. He knew I would never tell of his torture on me, for that would make me an even bigger weakling than I already was. The prospect of being revealed as such was even too much for me. After all I was a vertebrate with a spine and not some kind of slimy mollusk.

But I was also a bumbling fool and naïve to his well-designed plots that caused me much grief. A shining example: I was about 8, and at that age could barely keep my pee in without having to hold my weenie. After Friday mosque one evening Aleem invited me over to dinner. I liked going to Sultan Auntie's to eat, because her cooking style was very precise and elegant. Everything was in order, just so. The prawns were all the right size, big and fleshy, the white rice was steaming and fluffy, and the presentation was of museum quality. For someone like me who flubbed at anything mechanical, I admired and envied this handiwork. The best thing about Friday evening was that it would turn into Saturday. On Friday evening, school was at least two full days away, and I would be spared the ignominy of having no self-esteem and trying to play football or hockey with the more beefy, popular schoolmates who could run rings around me, if not push me over like a house of cards.

This Friday evening, the meal was Sultan Auntie's "special steak", tenderized with Papain and a mallet into succulent morsels that could slip down my gullet with a minimum of chewing. (Yes, I was one for avoiding exertion of any type; even chewing was a chore. The easier food slipped down to my stomach the better I thought it tasted).

After dinner, Aleem suggested that I have some milky coffee. Still a favorite coffee drink to this day, this concoction was basically a mug of hot milk into which one put a small teaspoon of Nescafe instant coffee, and two spoons of sugar. It was dessert and "good-night" milk all in one. Being the gullible nerd that I was, I didn't see Aleem slip an entire *tablespoon* of Nescafe. He gave me the cup, and I lapped it away like a thirsty cat. (One of the reasons I liked milk so much was because cute little kittens drank milk, and I wanted to be simpatico with them).

I was, now, of course wide awake. Aleem suggested we watch television. In Kenya, in those days, we only had one TV channel, and after the 9:30 PM news there was some kind of programming suited for older viewers. This being Friday night, I was allowed to stay up and watch. Mummy didn't mind, she knew I was just up the road in a compound guarded by two Askaris and so could walk home safely even if it was dark.

Now, typically I would be asleep within 5 minutes of the program. My siblings, my mother and I had this genetic predisposition of dozing just as any late night program started. But this time, in Aleem's house with the excess caffeine surging though my tiny head, I was very much awake. Aleem had purposely turned down the lights to induce fear as we watched a Hitchcock movie or an episode of *The Twilight Zone*. Whatever, it didn't' matter. Aleem knew what was going to be aired, – someone must have told him or he had read in the *Daily Nation's* listing. His trap was complete. I was wide awake, and we were going to watch some kind of scary horror perpetrated on an unsuspecting target. Aleem loved horror movies. He loved the haunting music, the bizarre plots, the violence and gothic darkness. I hated all of this. The scary parts frightened the crap out of me, and left indelible scars on my psyche. I would forever be followed by a mad ghost, or have my heart carved out for some strange ritual. When the scary parts came, Aleem liked to see the pain of fear on my face,. He would snigger and laugh, like that nasty Brutus in *Popeye*, my favorite cartoon.

After 40 minutes of Aleem's macabre enjoyment of my squirming, and when terror had almost given my tiny heart an attack, I decided to go home. I pleaded with Aleem to walk me home. I was way too scared to do this alone.

Aleem looked at me and burst out laughing. "No, go home yourself. Walk home and let the murderer also get you. You wanted to see a murderer, now is your best chance... Watch out for his knife."

I begged him again, but he was resolute. I would have to walk home. There are two routes from Aleem's flat to mine. One snaked around the curve of road where cars were parked on each side. The cars travelled in one direction, so if I walked this way I could benefit from any oncoming headlights. The other way, which was shorter, was to cut across through the middle-field but that would be much darker. I chose the road.

Holding my weenie, I began the treacherous journey home. I could run home, but that would make me a target. I surmised with my rational little brain that a runner has something to hide or is scared. That would likely set off the djinns, ghosts and vampires who prowled the night. It was better if I was casual about the whole thing. So I decided to walk nonchalantly. I even tried to whistle, but my mouth was too dry from fear. But with each step my confidence grew. As I turned the corner to the home stretch, I tried whistling again and managed to sound like an exhausted kettle.

My shrill sound was echoed by a more mellifluous whistle, rather like a warbler answering to a crow. Was I dreaming? Was there someone else out there? I held my privates even more tightly. The need to pee was immense. I must have been dreaming. I whistled again, and my sound was answered once more. I panicked and began to run the final 30 yards. As I passed flat #43 (My own flat was three doors down at #46) something in a dark shroud jumped from behind a car and screamed gutturally at me. The terror unleashed my pee. In an instant from the available light, I saw that it was Aleem wearing some kind of silly cape. He had wanted to terrify me, and he had succeeded. I just hoped he hadn't seen the streak of urine that was darkening the front of my pants. That was worthy of front page humiliation. I ran home and forced the key into the lock, as Aleem bellowed loudly gloating in his evil success.

Smoke

*M*y father was a smoker. My first recollection of his vile habit, probably at age 4, was of him holding a box of *Sportsman* cigarettes. I remember this, because that red package had a painting of a smiling race horse, that years later in college reminded me of that talking horse, Mr. Ed. Over the years, Papa graduated to more expensive forms of tobacco. First he went to the Embassy brand of cigarettes that claimed to be made from the finest Virginia tobacco. (Why Virginia, I had no idea then but I guessed it had to do with nymphs and sex). I clearly recall the end of the Embassy jingle from a movie theatre ad, where a group of successful black folk were having a party, playing musical instruments and blowing smoke rings at each other. "Smooth Embassy…. Choose the brand that comes first," the voice-over said. Smoking seemed like so much fun.

Apparently my father was as cool as the Negro band. Yes in those days we called black Americans, Negroes. It wasn't a slur for us. In fact it was a compliment and a way to distinguish between these suave black folk from the mostly illiterate "karias" from Wakamba or Kikuyuland.

Over the years as my father climbed up the income ladder, or he felt he had to keep up with his friends, he switched to the pricier *555 State Express brand*, and then later to *du Maurier*. The *du Maurier* came in an elegant square, red box. Compared to the other more rectangular shaped packaging, the *du Maurier* box was a piece of art. It opened and shut like a piece of fine furniture, and not the silly flip-top box all the other expensive cigarettes came in. Once open, the cigarettes were shielded by a thin aluminum or metal sheet stuck on to another thin sheet of paper. One of my personal challenges was to remove the ultra thin foil from its paper backing. When fully successful the stripped foil would look so eminently enticing when placed flat between books. It was like having a piece of brilliant silver. As kids we would collect these and use them as currency to trade for marbles or stickers.

It wasn't much surprise then that I wanted my dad to become a chimney. Each new box could yield silver, if I didn't shred the foil to tatters during the precise stripping operation. Since I needed as much as I could get my hands on to trade for goodies, there were several instances where I'd ask Papa to chain smoke his last few cigarettes in the box so that I could get at that valuable foil.

My mother thought that being a cigarette pusher was odd no matter what riches the foil could garner. When I was 8 Mummy made me promise that I would never smoke cigarettes. She said they were bad and cause one to cough horribly, spit blood and develop a disease called cancer. Lungs could turn all black inside and full of holes from cigarette smoke. This fear and a desire to please my mother made me promise to never smoke cigarettes. I kept this promise for a very, very long time.

Cancer was a recurring theme of discussion amongst the flats boys since it led to a gruesome, wasting death; the more devastating, the better. Among the surprising causes of cancer we documented, without any proof whatsoever, was the consumption of Fizzies. Fizzies were little cylindrical tablets that when placed in water would produce an effect similar to Alka-Seltzer. Upon contact with water, the Fizzies tablet would decompose into a sea of bubbles and turn into a splendid sugar drink. Actually most of us felt that the drink was mediocre, but the effect of watching bubbles created out of water was captivating chemistry. More so, when placed unbroken and directly on one's tongue the fizzy tablet caused a curious but pleasant, slightly burning sensation while releasing the sweet, artificial, lemon or orange flavor directly to the taste buds. Well, some smarty pants formed the opinion that we could get cancer from excessive Fizzies consumption. Pretty soon Fizzies use among us was condemned like contraband – you loved it but couldn't have it else your tongue would atrophy and your cheeks would become full of ugly holes. No one that I knew died to prove this theory, but I am sure the truth is out there somewhere.

My first foray with actual cancer causing sticks occurred when I was six or so. Behind each flat that circled our compound was an area called "back-of- flats". This area really was a two or three meter wide of mud, broken stone and storm drains that wound their way along the back wall of the entire compound. While narrow, this long, circular, and somewhat menacing ribbon allowed us to create our secret hiding spots in relative proximity of safety from our own houses. We could pretend to be on secret dangerous missions, deep in the African bush or Sahara desert, but still barely yards away from our mothers' aprons and a nice cold glass of Ribena. The back-of- flats were also a veritable mine for discarded items like used Durex rubbers, dull razor blades, and broken contraptions. For a young kid, the loot there was tantalizing. Cigarette butts of all types were also easy to find there. So my friend Alnashir (Nishu) and I wanted to find out what it was like to smoke. We found or stole a box of matches from his kitchen drawer, and went behind to the back of flats. We quickly collected ten or so butts, keeping all of them, just in case cigarettes did taste like heaven.

We lit up in quick succession. At first the cigarettes would not take. Nishu astutely noted that we had to suck on them. I agreed. My father was an expert cigarette sucker, so why I didn't I think of that? We both tried again taking a fresh set of stubs from the hoard we had placed in brown-paper bag. We sucked in deeply, and quickly felt the harsh smoke torture our lungs and felt the need to cough incessantly. Our eyes began to water, but we had done it. We had smoked our first cigarettes. It wasn't a fun experience but it allowed us to boast to our friends of our dangerous accomplishment.

It wasn't long after our fateful boast that Khanbhai's mother stopped us in the street. She wanted to know why we had urged Khanbhai to try and smoke. We protested that we had done no such thing. But with Khanbhai ratting on us, we knew we were in trouble. If Khanbhai's mother told our parents they would be livid for crossing the threshold into forbidden adulthood. The punishments we imagined would be horrific. We might have to repent in front of the mukhi-saheb (head of the mosque) and apologize publicly. This would make us into young pariahs from which recovery was impossible. Who knew, we might even be flogged on stage at the mosque. We knew that cigarette smoking by children was one of worst things a child could do. We lived in fear for the next few days, waiting for the axe to fall, but Khanbhai's mother, (God bless her) never ended up telling our parents.

Besides my cousin Aleem, Nishu was the friend I spent most time until the age of seven or so. He was full of mild mischief and we shared plenty of silliness, such as creating strange farting sounds and making fun of the vegetarian Hindus. How could they not eat meat? What kind of a religion didn't allow the killing of stupid little chickens to make into a delicious curry? The Hindus also believed in so many gods which was a complete anathema to our own young brainwashed minds smothered in Allah's omnipotence. How many gods did one need? We would note that even silly cows were Hindu gods and then burst out in laughter. We never tired of our own private jokes which also became our secret code of friendship.

But with Nishu there was a true sense of adventure and danger. As a spineless little boy, unwilling to carve out my own dangerous path, I was very much attracted to him. One evening, as dusk approached, we sauntered through the back-of-flats trying to squeeze every last bit of light. Nishu and I found ourselves staring at a huge mound of grass clippings and dead plants. These had been deposited by the gardener for our flats, Njoroge, a Kikuyu man with a friendly disposition. Nishu and I thought we would do him a favor, by burning this mound at the back of flats. In reality we really weren't that kind and only wanted to play with fire. (If we really wanted to be nice to him, we would not regularly clog some of the narrow drains in the flats with rocks and assorted debris). But we were determined to *help* so we each lit a match; I on one end of the grassy heap and Nishu on the other. We stood back as the huge fire roared quickly through the dry clippings. Flames rose ten feet high and we thought we would burn down the entire compound. I immediately thought of prison, and being separated for my mother. We debated if we should alert someone to call the fire brigade, but Nishu wanted nothing of that. If found out as a lead perpetrator he would be tied from limb to limb by his crazy father and whipped till he bled. Perhaps the fire would die. We didn't stand to find out and ran home.

From my bedroom window I could see the fire roaring away. Terrified, that I would be going to jail for setting off a blaze that would engulf all our houses, I moved away. I wasn't going to own up to anything, not yet anyway, so I stopped observing the crime scene as if watching it would directly link me to the dastardly deed. I then prayed and begged Allah to have the inferno die down. I recall promising servitude to anything he or my mother wanted me to do. I thought of including some of my father's wishes in this penance, but those would be too ornery, so I stopped at Allah and mum's.

Over the years I have found that the best way to ignore a disaster is by going to sleep. Perhaps this desire for somnolence in the face of adversity germinated that cool Nairobi evening. I told my mother I was tired and so shut my eyes without brushing my teeth. If there was to be an evacuation, my mum would get me. Falling asleep was easy for me, and this fateful day was no exception.

I woke up the next morning and in the early light leapt to the window to view the destruction I had caused. The fire had died down completely, with no visible sign of damage to life or property. All that remained was a wisp of smoke from the last of the smoldering remains. I leapt for joy, or more precisely, I did an internal somersault. (There was no way I could have physically done one; I didn't have the chops for that). God is indeed great! Allah u Akbar! Since it was also Saturday morning and there was no school, life had reached a certain zenith.

Flat # 28

Zaher Uncle was not really our uncle. He was my father's child-hood friend and drinking buddy and lived in flat # 28, one door down the hill from Sultan Auntie's # 27. But we called him uncle be-cause he was a lovely, kind man who adored my siblings and me. For years, he would visit us each Saturday night, bearing a gift of fresh fruit or chocolate. On many occasions he brought grapes that he purchased from Nairobi City Market. These delicious black orbs were a luxury for tropical Kenya and imported and air freighted from Greece. I know this for the wooden boxes carrying the plump, fleshy fruit had Hellenic mark-ings. That and since they also said quite clearly, "Produce of Greece".

I guess it wasn't the actual fruit that made us feel rich, but the fact we were eating something that had to flown in from the land of Minotaurs, Medusa and Zeus. Yes, grapes quickly became my favorite fruit, more so than any outrageously succulently papaya, insanely luscious mango, tangy passion fruit, or a panoply of other exquisite equatorial wonders. To me, *that* bounty was boring and so ordinary, present at dinner tables in almost every house I knew. No, the magic spheres from Greeks sent me in search of Odysseus and other Greek myths. I read these as quickly as Achilles could run. I loved Greek stories, and in my mind I was already an honorary Spartan.

In exchange for these great grapes and visions of travel he thrust upon us, we returned Zaher Uncle with simple adoration. We also pressed Mummy to ensure that the home cooked meals he ate with us were of the best possible variety. It wasn't necessary for us to do so; Mummy had a warm spot Zaher Uncle, and besides Pops would safely be boozing at home and not at some grungy bar with his group of lushes. So Saturday night dinners with Zaher Uncle were real feasts; curry with prawns twice the size of my index finger, "Kuku-Paka" or chicken in rich coconut broth, or spiced mincemeat with potatoes and fresh chapattis.

On Saturday night, both my mother and father were at home in a reasonable mood. Ferry and Rozy were at Zaher Uncle's feet or milling around my mother in the kitchen. I was probably reading a random volume of Encyclopedia Britannica, hoping to impress Zaher Uncle with a nugget of cool knowledge. All was right in the world, Saturday evenings were indeed homey and lovely.

The evening began by receiving the delightful grapes in a bunch and with us kids looking at its wonder. Why couldn't we grow grapes in Kenya? I found out grape growing was not suited to our tropical climate, even though Nairobi at 5,500 feet above sea level was far more temperate than the coast. I eventually learned that our drawback was that we weren't "Mediterranean" enough. Soon, lands boasting this special weather including Spain, Greece, New Zealand, Italy, California, and Chile held special appeal to me. Through the trusty set of Encyclopedia Britannica, I read and then dreamt of vineyards and olive groves, of the orange sun and fishermen in striped blue shirts coming smiling into a picturesque port with their daily catch. I loved anything related to the holy grape, and this is perhaps how I eventually developed my fondness of wine, and followed my father's footsteps to also become a lush. .

Papa and Zaher Uncle would start of the night of drinks and dinner with a beer typically a "Tusker Export". They would follow this with two or three "tots" of Johnny Walker Red, each with a splash of water, before Mummy served dinner. They talked about stuff adults talk about, and though I was not the one drinking, the alcohol induced gaiety suffused me with warmth.

Zaher Uncle was, as he put it, "a confirmed bachelor". There was no hint of him ever sharing his bed with a lover or a woman of ill-repute. As children, we were warned never to inquire why he didn't have a wife. He was a clean-cut man, who probably gave up on religion but didn't advertise it. He worked as an accountant for a securities trading firm called Dyer and Blair. He was diligent about work, leaving each morning at about 7:30 AM in his trusty Volkswagen beetle, and returning at 7 PM. His weekday dinners were supplied by our neighbor, Mrs. Daya, who was paid to fill a "tiffin", a portable steel box of several compartments in which to place the dinner. A typical meal would include dal, meat curry, rice, chapattis, and Kachumber (a tangy Indian salad). On Saturday he ate dinner with us, and on Sunday, he would eat both lunch and dinner somewhere in the city. It was a simple but honorable life.

Zaher Uncle's biggest contribution to my development was leading me away from communism. One Saturday evening when the 1971-73 Israeli – Egyptian war was in full swing, I'd just finished summarizing the BBC's shortwave broadcast of the day's events, when Zaher Uncle and I began to debate the merits of Communism. I noted that many Egyptian MiGs were down, and an even larger number of tanks destroyed. It was a sad time. Egypt, a Muslim country, with its anchor in the USSR appealed to me. I was on the side of Muslims, I said. I explained with great bravado that Egypt was right, mostly because they had the Russians supporting them. The Russians, I had read or heard, treated everyone equally. Now I was only 11, and I didn't know fuck from Adam. But I liked displaying my knowledge of war and ethics, gained either through the BBC, various Biggles books, British comics recounting World War II heroics and perhaps something smart Ivan Araujo, my favorite newscaster, might have once said on the Voice of Kenya. Anyway, I took a leaning to Marxism and Socialism, not knowing that they had also created the likes of Stalin and the Stasi.

Zaher Uncle was not impressed with me. He simply asked me this, "Would you like to have a doctor paid as well as someone who cleans the streets?" At first I didn't understand. Of course it made sense to my tiny, overactive but still developing brain that total equality would be foolish. If a barber could make as much money as a surgeon, then why in God's name was I studying? Was it simply to please my father in the shadow of that all-too-good cousin Aleem?

In a flash of understanding, I never turned back. Zaher Uncle *was* right, and I was now a full-fledged capitalist and supporter of Zionism. Many years later I read Richard Dawkins' *The Selfish Gene*, and realized how right Zaher Uncle had been. Cultivating DNA superiority was the only salvation of mankind, only of course until the smarties finally blow all of us up with uranium stuck up our world's (Ur)anus.

Saving me from joining the Red Army or going on a Chinese Death March, was not his single accomplishment of helping me put my head on straight. I was and am still indebted to Zaher Uncle for so much more. I felt a natural pull toward him. His life seemed so morose, with no wife to spoil him like my dad had in my mother.

One evening I asked Mummy why Zaher Uncle never married. Didn't he want to be fixed-up, like so many older bachelors I had encountered in the Mosque? Mummy looked at me and saw the love I had for the man. She told me to sit down.

There is a story," she said, "but you must keep it secret."

Oh, boy, oh, boy, a secret story! I crossed my legs on my mother's bed and waited in earnest.

"It all happened many years ago," she began. Zaher Uncle had gone to Europe on a trip. Anyway, he met this lovely German girl in some oddly named town like Baden-Baden. They liked each other a lot (Mummy's euphemism for making love) and spent every day together for a week. Then Zaher Uncle had to fly back; his vacation was ending and he has spent most of his money on drinks, flowers and gourmet treats like black forest cake. They left tearfully, saying goodbyes at the airport." It was special", they concurred but Mummy noted it that it simply couldn't last. With his beloved in Germany and Zaher Uncle in Nairobi their love was doomed.

Months later Zaher Uncle received a scarlet letter from his partner in this tryst. The German lady had become pregnant it said she was going to keep the baby. "Now," Mummy continued, "we couldn't marry non-Ismailis" - another stern reminder to keep my purity by avoiding Hindus, let alone someone who was white or black. But Zaher Uncle did the next best thing, Mummy said. He would support mother and child until he reached adulthood. And so he did. End of story.

What? I had all kinds of questions after that. What was the boy's name? Did Zaher Uncle ever see the boy? Did the woman ever get married? Did he miss her and his son? These were difficult questions for even my saintly mother to answer. So instead she replied, "Your questions don't add to the moral of the story."

Yikes! What was I thinking, where was my sensitivity? What a puddinghead I was. Mummy was right. This affair had to be buried with the dignity of silence. I only tell this story today, since Zaher Uncle has since passed. Perhaps, perhaps, there is some chance that his son might read this and know a wonderful man fathered him.

Boots

Football (soccer) was always my number one passion and the very reason I existed. To be the best, and eventually play for first division Arsenal FC in England, I needed a pair of real football boots. These would be made of leather and would have real studs on the soles for gripping. When I walked on hard surfaces, such as the cement footpath to the middle field, the boots would make reassuring, professional sounding clicks. In retrospect these sharp edged sounds befit a gaggle of secretaries rushing around tiled floors in high heels than a professional football player. But walking on the concrete toward our pitch would announce to the rest of my pals that I, *the anointed one* whose professional future was guaranteed, was coming to play. This was the power of real boots. Every boy I knew wanted a pair. Only a couple of very rich kids I knew had a pair. But these boys lived a few miles away in another compound (for richer folk) and did not count.

Our flats fielded a decent team with Sulu, Aloo, and Lalji anchoring as forwards, and we held practice sessions during our school holidays, after school, and on weekends. Other Indian kids in our area of Parklands also had teams of their own, and we formed an informal league with matches played on occasional Saturdays. We didn't play with young African (Black) boys, because we didn't really know any except for a fortunate handful at primary school who could afford to pay the modest school fees. These African boys did not live close by anyway, so the issue was moot. But even if they did we would have opted not to mix. The Africans were always better athletes than us Indians and this would make the matches unfair, strip away our fun and ruin our fantasies of turning professional.

Our team was called the Highridge Eleven. Besides the forward line who had some skill and Shiraz Virjee (nicknamed Cockeyed) who was a robust back, the rest of us were a bunch of rag-tag, tiny misfits. Cockeyed was one of my better friends and had a very lazy eye. He also had thick strong thighs and was fearless which allowed him to stand up to any slinky forward. As goalkeeper, this meant I had a good defensive wall which made me look good. It was hard for anyone to score when Cockeyed was playing back. Cockeyed was also bright and we could discuss advanced topics such as goal differences, home-away records, and games in hand without inflicting boredom on each other. The other boys were simply not as cerebral as us. Cockeyed's mother and mine were close friends and had regular gabfests extolling the virtues of God, and how best to please him/her. This was an added reason why we were friends. But perhaps best of all, he didn't tease me or make fun of my lack of talent. As gratitude, I offered him my unrelenting friendship.

But back to the important business of boots: these were really necessary for me to excel so I brought my argument to the dinner table. Why would anyone deny me the right to become a professional football player? I had to quickly develop the skills for subtle touches, brilliant strikes and clever passes. To do this I needed boots. There was a direct correlation between the number of professionals who wore boots versus those who used lowly "tennis" or canvas shoes. In fact, I knew of no footballer on TV who used tennis shoes. Case closed.

My father nodded his head back and forth and smirking, as if to say, "What are we going to do with this little dreamer boy? He thinks boots will make him better. What a joke! He needs to get stronger, put on more weight and train if he wants to go anywhere." I recognized the scorn in his half-smile, but I was determined.

"Papa," I asked, getting the rare fortitude to question my Dad, "When you play tennis, do you wear your gum shoes or chappals (flip-flops)?" Pops was one of the better tennis players in the entire country. This earned him a status of sports king, minor hero and someone to be admired among us boys.

"Aaah....," said the minor sports celebrity dismissively, "shoes alone will get you nowhere. When I was young, many of us played barefoot football. And, by the way I was quite good. I was quick and had an accurate left foot. I played for my high school team. First learn how to play well without shoes before wasting all that money"

Mummy, ever protective of her little sweet boy, asked me how much the boots cost. (Great! I was breaking down the resistance. Getting Mummy's support meant I was almost halfway there. I couple of more teary pleadings and I could almost smell the fresh leather).

From my many reconnaissance missions into the city centre, I knew the boots were priced at 120 shillings at Nairobi Sports House. This was where Papa bought his own tennis rackets and so we might get an additional discount, I pointed out cleverly.

"A hundred twenty shillings! What do you think there is a money plant in this house? Do you think I'm made of money? Do you think I have a gold mine?"

Clearly Pops was getting a bit irate. The nostrils flared on his very large nose, the hook prominent and possibly pulsating. I thought of telling him, "Well your nose *is* a diamond mine. You pick at your nose all day, as if there were priceless gems in there". But my balls were and still are relatively tiny and I remained silent. If I muttered anything in defense, I would leave myself exposed to an hour-long lecture on the value of money and its role in keeping family harmony. Papa's lectures inflicted more pain than waterboarding or nail pulling.

"How many boys do you know who wear such expensive boots?"

I sensed my advantage slipping but I couldn't lie to my father now. Any falsity would be grounds for an immediate dismissal of my request. "I know of two boys who have them."

"Who are these boys?"

"Moez and Nadeem Karsanji," I muttered.

"The Ismail-Karsanji children," Papa shrieked, his voice sharpening uncharacteristically from its usual cigarette-induced baritone. "Of course they can afford silly luxuries! Don't you know they are sons of multi-millionaires? I have to work hard for my salary; I don't have a gold mine like they do!"

I looked at my mother, who pinched pennies every which way to stash away some savings. She had the smile of consolation on her. I knew that to pursue this further, I would be hurting her even more. So with a resigned look, I nodded slowly to temporarily acknowledge the loss of my plea.

But I was a crafty little bugger. When Zaher Uncle came in the next Saturday for drinks and dinner, I lobbied for his support. "Zaher Uncle," I asked in a level tone, "when people go to war, if they don't have the right equipment, such as the right swords and guns, they usually fail, don't they?" Papa turned up his eyebrows. He smelled something fishy, but didn't quite get my weasel move and did not interrupt.

"Well, it depends," said Zaher Uncle wisely. "A lot depends on strategy and tactics. Even an ill-outfitted army, can win great battles, for example, with the element of surprise"

"Oh for God sakes," I screamed in my head, "a simple yes would have done fine."

"But," Zaher Uncle continued, "For evenly matched tacticians with similar sized armies, I would agree that is true." Phew... not all was lost.

Papa, wanting to unearth the real reason, asked, "Why do you want to know?"..... A-ha, my opening, at last.

"Well, you see, to become a professional footballer, I will need boots, that is I need the right equipment."

"Again with the silly boots! Didn't we go over that?" Papa's voice was at the edge of reason. Absolutely no boots! My decision is final."

Well that approach didn't go too well, and I slinked upstairs to "get my storybook" rather than succumb to another lecture on the time value of money. I had lost. I had put up a brave fight, but I learned a lesson today; that bravery could be self-destructive. But it still seemed so unfair. Ferry got all kinds of dresses for every silly little religious occasion, but I had to beg for something that was vital for my development and worldly stature.

Of course Ferry got what she wanted. After all she was Papa's favorite. A precocious, charming, funny, intelligent beautiful girl, she had everything going for her. At heart, all I really wanted to do was make my Dad proud; to show him that I could be as good at football as he was in tennis. In an oddly sinister way, for some reason, he didn't wanted me succeed. I pondered about that until a massive realization hit me. My father hated me. That's what it was, pure hate. Why else would he not want his son to have immense success? I strapped on this emotional baggage, ready to carry it for decades.

I didn't mention boots again for a whole week. When Zaher Uncle next came in for Saturday dinner, he didn't bring any fruit. What, no grapes, no peaches? Gosh another disappointment. What a bad week it had been. Sensing my disappointment he said rather quickly "No fruit today, but here is something else." He held out a rectangular package covered in brown paper. I opened it rashly, exposing the brilliant blue box with three stripes.

Was I dreaming? No, I realized, I wasn't. My future was guaranteed. In a display of utmost generosity I was staring at a pair of the most beautiful objects ever made. The leather on them was real and soft. The laces were a deep black; ascetic and inspiring. The undersides were molded of the strongest creamy-white plastic I had ever seen. The studs were prominent and proud, exuding both power and sturdiness. I could kiss and marry these things. I didn't mind. Then there were the stripes – the diagonal pieces of white leather that graced both sides of each boot with unspeakable elegance. "Din Tin Riemen" was written in German on the box. I took this to mean the three stripes, but never fully confirmed. These stripes were the secret ingredients of success. They were so smart and handsome, turning young footballers into carriers of glory, permitting rocket shots with considerable accuracy. This was the magic of Adidas.

I thanked Zaher Uncle profusely. Papa, I thought, was sneering at the possibility of my transformation and Mummy, looked at her little boy with the pleasure only mothers can have.

I didn't try on the boots. I couldn't risk scratching the gorgeous hide just yet. Instead I wrapped them back into the thin tissue paper. I had to be with heaven-sent perfection for a little while longer. Everything was sacred about this. I kept the box under my bed, reaching over to look at them with awe every time I could. Ferry had strict instructions not to come within five feet of the sanctum else I would rip all her fine dresses to shreds. (She knew I was serious). Rosy couldn't even walk yet, so she posed no threat of turning sacrilegious.

My love affair with the boots continued at a torrid pace. They would speak to me; throw off holograms of scissor and bicycle kicks and of the most unimaginable saves. There was one particular dream sequence where, as goalkeeper, the boots propelled me to make a diving save from one end of the goal post to the other. My opponent was Jairzinho, a teammate of Pele's whose strikes often curved like a banana. He kicked the ball hard from the left wing about 20 yards away. As I protected the near post, the ball had a mind of its own and traced the arc of an impossible ellipse. I had no choice but to dive at full extension as if into a sea of deep water. By God's grace and the powers of the boots, my finger tips thrust the ball beyond the far post. All of this was caught in my mind's eye, and still stands as the greatest save ever made. I didn't care that it was fantasy. With my magic boots anything was possible.

I think I finally tired of making love to these beautiful specimens of German handiwork after a week of non-stop snogging. I had caressed them into certain suppleness – at least so I thought. This inanimate pair of footwear had received so much adoration from me that Ferry hinted that I might soon be getting another pair of baby boots. What? What was she talking about? I didn't have full knowledge of the birds and bees just yet, so I ignored her kooky observation. As if caressing even magic boots, would create new ones out of thin air? I *wasn't* going to be a magician until I put the boots on.

So the sacred day came. It was a bright Nairobi Saturday morning. The lack of rain the past few days meant that the football pitch would be hard and dry. None of that horrible red, thick mud would be present to cake my boots. Although for an instant that did appeal to me, for professionals often had mud on theirs. But like a new bride or car – as someone much older had once remarked – one didn't want to test the ferocity of passion too soon. I wanted to make sure that I eased gently into them.

The temperature was just right and I wouldn't sweat excessively though my bright new white socks that I had stolen from my father's tennis clothes drawer. The effect of smart white anklets held up by the gorgeous black leather with the luminescent diagonal white stripes would, I was sure, blind the opposing team's forwards. Of course I didn't walk the 15 minutes to the pitch with my boots on. That would have been silly and damaging. Instead I needed to announce them to the world like a stunning Georgian debutante. So I took the blue box and put into a brown paper bag and to the sporting club where we had a huge match with "Lags Eleven". This was the team from the 3rd Parklands Avenue compound, and Adil and Moez Karsanji would be present. Ha! Let them try and outshine my boots!

When I arrived, I said, "Hey Guys look what I got." I brought out the blue box with the boots wrapped in the tissue paper. My teammates were suitably impressed and soon I was holding audience like a king showing off a new species of bird. Everyone wanted to touch the magic. Sulu and Aloo, our captain and vice captain respectively, were almost drooling.

Sulu said, "Let me play with them, you are only the goal keeper!"

I replied with a surprising and steadfast vigor that I would make great dives and saves for the team. Besides they were mine so I was going to wear them. Aloo tried to convince me to give them up for the team by promising me three goals if I let him wear them. But I was resolute. *I would wear them while playing goalie. I would be the team's savior, not him.* "Just watch my saves."

The boots fit snugly. They were actually too snug, but I ignored the pinching. I was in goal and a beautiful sight to behold: my feet were gorgeous, I had a professional looking countenance and my spectacles allowed a Zen-like focus. I slapped my hands together, graced them with my spit and was ready for kick-off.

We scored early; a mistake by Lags Eleven's center back who let Sulu through easily. We quickly went up 2-0 on another mistake capitalized by Aloo. I had already made a daring save by hanging on Cockeyed's coat tails. The big back allowed everything to slow down to a glacial pace in front of my goal, giving me plenty of time to assess a tricky situation and calmly pluck the feet of the opposing team's striker. It was indeed a Gordon Banks moment. As play continued, the hurt in my feet ratcheted, sending jabs of pain through my back. But I persevered. I was simply breaking the boots in and the glory to be had by winning was more than enough to compensate.

Then everything went wrong. Cockeyed sprained his ankle and we brought on Minu to substitute for him. But Minu who was five inches shorter and 30 pounds lighter than everyone else on the field. He ran away from the attackers and not toward them. In quick succession I let in five quick goals before half time, most of which could have been easy saves, but I was too slow to react in each case. I did the only thing a self respecting professional could ever do: I blamed my boots. When I removed the socks at half time my feet were bloody and raw. "See, the boots were too tight."

I got some sympathy but not enough to cover the five egregious mistakes I had made. Aloo asked if he could try my boots on for size. He said his feet were smaller than mine. I gave them to him, and he went on to score two more goals. I returned to goalie with my tennis shoes on, this time not embarrassing myself into oblivion. We finally lost 6 to 4, and I knew my football career was over. Yet I swore to find another outlet for my sporting genius. Perhaps table tennis, tennis, cricket or even snooker as soon I was 14; the minimum age for playing on any one of the fine three snooker tables at our club. And, yes, I let Aloo keep the magic boots.

Sex Vol. # 1

After my debacle as goalkeeper, the slow footed and gloriously clumsy Ali Nurali replaced me on the first team. The decision by the most influential team members, Aloo and Sulu, made sure of that. Now, not only was I not the regular goalkeeper, but Aloo got to keep my boots. Didn't he realize that my giving away of the boots should be construed as a bribe? Where was the decency among rogues?

While I didn't have a choice in the matter I wasn't going to get embarrassed into ignominy. So I launched into technical gobbledy-gook and mouthed off about one-two passes, and formations of 5-3-2, and 4-2-4, that Arsenal and other leading football teams used. Then I asked if I could be team coach instead. The guys thought about it for a second, and then decided I could do no harm if I was *outside* the pitch, rather than *in* it. I argued that I could draw up precise diagrams to build an attack or prevent goals from corner kicks. When Aloo chimed in by saying it was a good idea, I became, possibly, the youngest football coach in the country. It was an honor I said to be their coach and nodded to Aloo that his support was compensation enough for the boots I had donated to him.

Of course no one paid attention to my elaborate diagrams. It is harder coaching a bunch of 10 – 12 year olds on the merits of organized play than it is to make fish dance. But all that didn't matter; I had saved face and was one of the guys again.

My extensive knowledge of football was garnered through comics. My two favorites when I was football crazy were *Tiger* and *Scorcher* published out of Fleet Street in London. These magazines were filled with stories of great fictional footballers who toiled through injury and hardship but eventually managed to win the FA Cup or the League Championship. They also alternated full page color photographs of real giants such as Allan Clarke (Leeds), Bobby Charlton (Manchester United) and team photos of recent champions. When any really famous Arsenal player appeared, for example Frank McLintock, I ripped out the page and stuck it on my bedroom wall. I soon ran out of wall space because a huge poster of the 1970 World Cup winners' (Brazil) side dominated my side of the wall. By Papa's decree, largely pushed through at Ferry's insistence, I was only allowed to place posters directly above the head of my bed. So, cool Arsenal stars such as Charlie George and Ray Kennedy were left out. Gosh, how I hated Ferry and her way to get things done in her favor.

The year was 1972 and I was barely twelve. While my aspirations to turn professional had taken a severe beating, I decided to make amends by being the best coach I could possibly be. This, of course, meant diligent analysis of the comics' illustrations. I could easily copy the most intriguing of these and make them into instructional diagrams for my role as coach. In short order, I had diagrammed several plays that if executed correctly would guarantee goals.

I think I was the only boy who had a standing weekly comics order at Woolworth's. This gleaming beacon of Nairobi commerce and diagonally across the street from the fashionable New Stanley Hotel, served as the newsagent for Kenya's expatriate community. There one could get every conceivable worldly newspaper and magazine. I remember admiring the tissue-thin broadsheet, *The Observer* and aptly named *News of the World*. But my favorite paper was the *Sunday Telegraph*, which had I thought had the best football coverage.

Each Saturday morning I would take an early #12 Bus from outside the flats, pay my 20 cent fare, and head off to the City Centre. The bus would take me past my primary school, the club and mosque, and City Park before reaching the suburbs of Ngara. After Ngara, the bus entered a giant circle of concrete that spanned the Nairobi River and which fed into three different parts of the city. The bus would take the first branch and soon drop us across from the main Fire Station on Government Road. The walk to Woolworth's on Kimathi Street was then accessible by a straightforward walk through an alley.

Shanti, a balding Indian guy with a soft, milky complexion and of indeterminate adult age, ran the newsagent stand. For regular customers, Shanti would set aside issues to be picked up. He was always glad to see me and would hand over my comics rolled up neatly with a rubber band. My eyes would light up as I would see the package; it reflected the great sensuality of the moment, of getting the next installment of so many favored comic strips. One of these was the madcap adventures of the Swiss Family Robinson, a third division team with uniforms that uncannily looked like Arsenal's red and white. Managed by a fat crazy granny and captained by Pa Robinson, the team was quite successful at pulling off major upsets during cup competitions.

I walked outside after thanking Shanti and handing over my shillings, and quickly removed the rubber band. I raced to find the section of Swiss Family Robinson in *Tiger*. Last week's issue left me hanging at a crucial spot in the FA cup, and I wanted to find out what happened. It turned out that my team did go on to win, so I smiled broadly at no one in particular.

But out of the corner of my eye, I spotted a strange looking man staring at me with eyes set very wide apart. He was a tall Somali with crinkly hair and a grungy coat. He seemed transfixed by my outfit of long pants and swank long sleeved shirt that I always reserved for Saturday.

Yes, I knew I was hip and looked the part but would that creep stop staring at me? I looked away and walked toward the traffic circle at Kenyatta Avenue and Kimathi Street. Arguably, the prettiest intersection in Nairobi, it also meant that I would have to wait for a stop light before I could cross. The red light spoke to the cars and I began to cross on the "Zebra crossing" or pedestrian cross walk. From behind, "Creepy Somali Guy" (CSG), tapped me on the shoulder and then winked at me with those bizarre, evil eyes. What? What did he want? I didn't have much money on me but it was mine, via a difficult session of pleading and negotiating with Mummy so he simply couldn't have it. As long as I was in a crowd or in a store, I'd be OK.

All the reading I had done on child sleuths (courtesy of the incomparable Enid Blyton), kicked into gear. I decided I would have to lose this possible thief. So I walked quickly into a large store that sold curios such as animal woodcarvings, lion claws set in gold, and zebra skins. I pretended to be interested in buying something and after much thoughtful browsing, I left without any purchase. Having safely shaken off the thief, I walked out back to the street. I had gone no further than a few steps, when CSG reappeared.

He winked at me again and said, "Babu Chale" (Let's go, little boy).

His rough, large hand grabs and pulls at my shoulder. In a flash CSG was holding my palm, pulling me along. At first I was too stunned to react and let him drag me. I then tried to wriggle free but his grip was strong. I found that my tongue was also of no use. We were heading to the poorer part of town where cheap hotels were available for the hour. This wasn't good. I knew CSG wanted to rob and kill me.

I tried my voice again, but it was nothing more than a minor peep. I tried once more shouting, "NO!" This attempt was better. While not a full-fledged hair-raising alarm, it was enough for CGS to lessen his grip. I wriggled free and bound into another store and the immediate safety of musical instruments and music records. My detective/ spy switch at full tilt, I began admiring a pair of drums and some album covers. If one looked interested, one might be buying something. How long could I fool the shopkeeper before he found out I wasn't going to buy anything? I knew I needed time to tire out my pursuer.

Then I saw this album: *Captain Fantastic and the Brown Dirt Cowboy*. My much elder cousin Abeed had raved about this one particular artist, and he had a cassette tape of this. Yes! A breakthrough! Now, if questioned by the long-haired shopper's assistant, I could at least pretend to know about the music.

As any vendor knows, it can take a while before a kid makes up his mind with the money he has squirreled. An album is an important purchase and not to be taken lightly. As long as one didn't handle the vinyl, we could stare at the album cover till drool landed somewhere. The silly thing is, Ferry and I didn't even have a record player, so the issue was moot. I wasn't going to buy an album let alone a drum set, but I needed the safety of the store until the coast was clear.

As palpable minutes ticked away, I began to get some strength. For prolonged shelter, I now knew that I had to ask complex questions of the shopper's assistant, "Was this album in Stereo?"

"Yes, yes of course it is in Stereo. Big rock stars are always in Stereo." The assistant dealt me a mean sneer, as if I had asked if Mombasa was the capital of Europe.

"How many instruments on the record?" I asked, pinching the bottom of my chin to make me look pensive and a true scholar of pop music.

"Instruments? Why would you want to know about instruments?"

I decided to go for broke. "Well I want to learn how to play one of the songs on guitar. So I need to know which one to buy," I lied, my voice assuming the nasally whine of a spoilt rich little boy, like Moez Karsanji.

The assistant saw not just an album sale, but a guitar and possibly lessons. "You know I give lessons, as well. I play lead guitar for a local band. I could teach you".

The hard sell was on, and I had to play along or be accosted by CSG. I took my chances with Guitar boy. I didn't know much about rock music, for I was too young to give a shit about dancing and girls. But I needed an excuse.

"What guitar do you play?"

"A Fender Stratocaster. It's the best."

"How good is the best?"

"Anyone who is anyone uses a Fender. Best in the world."

"OK, may I please see one?"

It's at the storeroom in the back," he said, his glare assessing my ability to pull off such a purchase. "We don't keep them out here. They are the best," he reminded me.

"Well my birthday is coming up and I think my Dad might buy it for me if I ask him nicely." At any early age I noticed that, when necessary, I could take the art of fibbing to another level.

As Kobe Bryant might say today, "When the chips are down, I elevate my game."

Guitar Boy went searching behind. I moved slowly and stealthily to the window; a fox, but still very much prey. No sign of CSG. I took a deep breath, and walked out of the store. CSG had really left. YES! I ran all the way to the bus stop home.

Later that evening, in the shadows thrown by the orange Nairobi moon, I recounted my story to my mates on the steps of the middle-field. I spoke with bravado. "Boy did I outfox that thief."

Aly Khan, a year older than me, began to laugh uncontrollably. "He wanted to give you sperm. He didn't want to rob you!"

"Why would he want to give me sperm? That's what husbands give to their wives." I was now old enough to know a bit about baby making and how a very naughty word called "fucking" had a role to play in this strange mélange with sperm.

"I know all about sperm," Aly Khan boasted confidently. "Let me tell you what happened to me three Saturday nights ago....." The secret of sperm was going to be revealed to us. The Nairobi air at 5,500 feet above sea level was dry and cool; the stars bright enough to spot any hyenas or big kitties in the dark. Alnashir, Virani, Lalji, Khanbhai were transfixed, and I had goose bumps the size of cysts.

Aly Khan, a couple of years older than me didn't live in our compound, but every so often, when he wanted to hang, made the short jaunt to our middle-field from his house five minutes away. While he wasn't the brightest of bulbs, Aly Khan wasn't a dimwit. Like most boys, he loved a rapt audience and our coterie of four juniors was precisely where he could reveal his own secret.

He began by first reminding us that we were still kids, and this was now adult talk. To us, peach-fuzzed and still carrying baby fat, Aly Khan had crossed over the Rubicon of adulthood. He was heroic and accordingly had the right to a condescending tone. He first set the scene by boasting about dance parties he often frequented with his friend Jayesh. These dance events paid by rich parents were held at swanky hotels such as the Panafric or Intercontinental. Many of these were disguised as birthday parties for those turning 16 or 18. Aly Khan noted there was a lot of kissing and fondling at these clubs especially during slow dances. He went to describe his eyewitness accounts of buttocks and breasts being squeezed. At first he had thought this groping in the dark was funny, but after a couple of parties he began to enjoy how guys pressed their fronts to the girls.

On this particular night, his best friend Jayesh decided to hitch an early ride with one of his older cousins. Aly Khan said that Jayesh was drunk. He had two beers and he was falling all over the place. We were all shocked. Yes we knew Jayesh was in high school, so he had some more mature rights. But we didn't think drinking was one of them? Didn't the fool know that drinking beer was one of the world's foremost dangers?

"Two whole beers," Khanbhai exclaimed. "Wow! He must have been so drunk."

Virani, whose father was a complete lush, said, "Two beers is nothing. I've seen my father drink four or five beers at one go."

"Don't be a liar. No one can drink five beers. Your stomach would explode," Lalji shouted.

Aly Khan, sensing a tangential discussion brewing, said firmly. "I saw it with my own eyes. He had two beers and he started singing like a madman." That piece of crucial information stopped our bickering. Experimentation with the taboo that was alcohol led one to the express track to hell. And while some of our dads drank enough to get first class tickets on any rocket ship, we were now stupefied: sperm and beer in one narrative. Could it ever get better than this?

Aly Khan was back in control, his story gaining legitimacy in light of Jayesh's exploits. He continued, "I decided to stay. Man these girls loved to be squeezed on the dance floor. It's so dark during slow dances that the girls think they can't be seen. But I tell you, some of those boobs were being squeezed like a cow's."

We sniggered in the dark. Boob squeezing seemed to an important precursor to this story on sperm. Why on earth would girls like their tits squeezed?

"When the party ended," Aly Khan went on, "I knew I had to walk to the city centre to find a lift home. But you know how far it is from the Panafric to the City Centre? Instead I looked around to see if I know someone who can give me a ride. I don't know anyone, they are much older. So I begin to walk. As I walk down the winding road from the ho-tel, a Goan chap stops his car. He asks if I want a lift. I said yes. Goan guy says his name is Fernandez, and he lives in Parklands. Wow, I think this is lucky. I can get home before three AM!"

"Where in Parklands?" Lalji pipes up, seeking every morsel of detail to this juicy story.

"He said he would drop me off near the hospital. From there, the walk to my house is only ten minutes. Then Fernandez asks if I like girls. 'Of course I like girls', I say. "I like squeezing their breasts until milk comes out."

"Fernandez laughed. He asked, 'Have you ever seen sperm, Aly Khan?'

"I shook my head. Then Fernandez asked me to open the compart-ment, pull out a magazine covered in brown paper, and open it to any page".

Khanbhai couldn't stop himself, "Did the magazine have naughty pictures?"

"Were they blueprints?" I asked, professing to know all about serious pornography. I added, "You know you can go to jail for seven years for having blueprints."

"Of course they were blueprints. Don't you think I know the difference?" scolded AlyKhan. "This stuff was hot."

"So what happened?" asked Lalji, his eyes bulging with anticipation. We were on the precipice of a new boy discovery, and it couldn't come too soon.

"Well, Fernandez stops by the side of a road. It's dark outside, so he leaves the inside car-light on for me to look at the magazine. Boy I have never seen such big tits on one woman! Another picture showed several men and women naked. Some were pressing against each other. The guys' cocks were huge and some of the girls had pink nipples".

We were four young-'uns about to discover the key mystery of the universe, and boy, were we ready. We were hanging on to every word.

"Fernandez then unzipped his trousers, and his own cock jumped out of his underwear. Really, it just jumped out! There were all these horrible curly black hairs around it."

"Then what happened, what?" Khanbhai panted, as if the secret of the Dead Sea scrolls were about to be revealed.

"Fernandez asked, if I wanted to touch his cock. It was so yucky, a little crooked but big."

"Did you touch it," Lalji asked?

"Of course I didn't touch it! But he then told me to watch as he held his cock with his right hand and moved it around a bit. Then all of a sudden, he made a noise and this white, milky liquid flew out of his cock and landed on his lap. It was weird.

"Fernandez, took a tissue from a box, wiped off the milk, zipped his fly, smiles and said to me 'That was sperm.'"

"You are dreaming." says Lalji our resident skeptic whose father was a chiropodist. "My dad says sperm is colorless and so tiny you can't even see it. And also sperm makes babies, and that only happens when a sperm goes into a woman. So, no woman means no sperm."

Lalji's argument made sense, and I said, "Maybe Fernandez has Bilharzia and his pee was just that way."

"It was sperm I tell you," Aly Khan insisted. Khanbhai, Lalji, Virani and I looked at each other with narrowed eyes. All of us knew Aly Khan was fibbing. Our evening of enlightenment had ended with no new clear understanding of sperm, breasts, and why some people had such big cocks.

Supplements

When I left Highridge for College, at the splendorous age of almost 19, I was 6 feet tall. I also weighed 117 pounds fully clothed. Despite many attempts to beef-up my physique during my teen years, I was among the skinniest of rakes this side of the Greenwich Meridian. In the *Daily Nation* I had seen pictures of poor souls hit by famine or war, in Somalia, Bangladesh or Biafra. It was clear to me that I looked only slightly better than these wastrels starved by the idiocy of bureaucrats and trumpeters of war.

I was once called "Biafra Child" by Lalji, which embarrassed me to no end. In fact my entire psyche, the very essence of my being, and, consequently, the conundrum of youth, revolved around gaining weight. I simply couldn't put on any weight, no matter how much I tried.

Mummy was the first to spot my predicament. When I was six she decided to get rid of the "worms" in my stomach. She was convinced that parasites were nesting somewhere in the goo of my insides, eating away the nutrients she fed her beloved and only boy. These naughty critters were creating happy slimy families of dancing threadworms or roundworms and would not give up. Her diagnosis for this rested on two pieces of evidence: my incessant need to scratch my anus, and my spindly physique. Wherever I was, I found my hand going to the crack of my (usually) khaki shorts which I would rub furiously until the itchy feeling passed. In a few minutes the itchiness would return and I would recommence the rubbing process. This was a source of much embarrassment to my mother, and to a lesser extent for me. (After all, which little boy didn't want to have a cool disease he could boast about?)

So we went to our family physician, a kind but ubiquitous Dr. Patel, who, after catching me with a rabid bit of ass-scratching at his dispensary, agreed with Mummy's diagnosis. Dr. Patel prescribed a powder of some sort that I was to dissolve in water and drink three times a day. It was the vilest thing. To this day, whenever I need a dose of bile to burn my gullet, I simply bring back that horrid smell and taste from the deep recesses of my brain stem.

The doctor said I should notice some white or pasty-looking thread-like creatures in my feces. My mother, God bless her soul, would come to the toilet after a potty to lay bare her angst at these creatures that had nothing better to do than to torment her little boy. Well, neither she nor I could find anything alive or wriggling in my shit. But Mummy insisted I finish the regimen, and so I did, vomiting a few more times before it was over. Unfortunately, for my mother and me, the scratching returned. We went back to the doctor, my mother almost in tears, and I – well, shit, I actually liked scratching my ass – was enamored by all this attention over me. The doctor ordered me to remove my pants. He spread my brown cheeks apart and shone a flashlight into my inner recess and laughed out loud.

It was a chilling, blood-curdling kind of laugh that only the very mean can achieve. He looked at my mother and said, "The reason your boy is scratchy is because he doesn't clean himself well enough after doing potty."

"I'm sorry, I don't understand," replied Mummy.

In an even tone, the doctor said, "Your boy simply has a filthy habit. All he has to do is wipe his "ghand" well after doing his business."

Doctor Patel was right, of course. For the next several weeks, dear Mummy took it upon herself to give me spot-checks on my cleaning habits. Only great mothers would do that. Shortly after learning how to really use toilet paper and wash myself in the shower, the itching stopped. The doctor was a genius, said my mother, and now she hoped her son would become a wee bit chubbier.

Alas, this was not to be. For one thing I hated chewing food. It took too much work. The kind of food I liked was the very soft kind, like rice, ripe bananas, or bread soaked in milk. The effort of moving one's teeth up and down, like a masticating cow, bored me and was tiring. The effort simply wasn't worth it. I wasn't a foodie in the adult sense of the word. I simply ate to live. Please don't get me wrong, I loved soft plain things such as ice cream, runny eggs and mango puree that could be swallowed without the labor of chewing.

But anything overtly chewy I stared with disdain on the dinner table. As meat-eating Muslims, Mummy would take pains trying to make the meat soft enough for me to swallow. She used papain to tenderize beefsteak, and pressure cooking to yield succulent lamb morsels that almost melted in the mouth. The operative word here is almost. Because there was still some chewing to do, the game I played with myself was to see how little I needed to chew.

One lunch, I swallowed a piece of meat large enough to stick in my throat. The Heimlich maneuver wasn't necessary to spare me, for I coughed harshly, launching a projectile of meat that landed near my father's plate. To describe his ensuing rage simply as rage does not do him justice. In the immediate instant that followed, Papa's eyes bulged into cow-like orbs, his ears acquired a very fresh hue of deep red, and his handsome face was locked in an internal debate to explode or let this unfortunate misgiving pass. Of course, he blew up.

"What the bloody hell are you doing?" he barked.

Mummy's protective glare, however, silenced him quickly. So instead of continuing on a rant he simply walked off the table, the offending piece of meat still by his plate. I knew I would have to pay for this with a lecture at some point, but any delay was good.

Getting me to gain weight was more than a herculean task for Mummy. She never succeeded. If today she found out that today her boy sported a pronounced double-chin, she would be a very happy Mom-in-Heaven. But at home, Mummy would ingloriously try to fatten me by preparing special platters that might pique my appetite. These ranged from my short term fancy for cow brains or chicken kidneys in red curry, or goats' hooves in spicy gelatinous broth, to the fairly more mundane bananas in milk.

My own furious attempts at looking less like a string began when I was 14. By this age, I had personal experience which confirmed that larger muscles do indeed garner more respect from one's peers. I hated conflict, wore thick glasses and looked like a small, skinny duck. Life was one trial after another of not angering boys bigger than me. This strategy was successful but not entirely, and I had multiple moments being on the receiving end of boy rage and sadism. It didn't help that I was compared to Piggy in *Lord of the Flies.* So on occasion, I had to endure punishment like the padding in a prison full of young miscreants.

Once, for altogether no reason, someone who I thought was a friend of mine practiced his karate chop on my face, sending my glasses flying, and breaking them in two. I did nothing to retaliate, except perhaps to smile sheepishly. Another incident was even more humiliating. My long time pal, Ladka, a fun-filled fat boy, thought it would be fun to anger one of the Mosque's more notorious bullies at my expense. Ladka informed the bully that I was teasing his sister. Well of course, that didn't go over too well and I was slapped around like some transgressing slut angering her pimp.

Was there nothing I could do about it? Fight back, someone once said to me. I knew I was a weakling but I wasn't stupid. I had the beginnings of in an interesting, but non-ugly face, and if I could hold the zits at bay, there was a slim chance that one day I might land a girlfriend. I didn't need to abandon my path to puppy love bliss for some fool-hardy display of getting my face re-arranged.

It also didn't help that in the previous holidays, members of our Aga Khan Club (AKC) Nairobi had travelled to Mombasa to compete against other Aga Khan Clubs from Mombasa, Dar-es-Salaam, Kampala and elsewhere in East Africa. Friendly but heated battles in soccer, snooker, cricket, badminton, tennis, volleyball, and table tennis would decide the title of Best Overall East African Aga Khan Club.

At the matches we always cheered on our city or town. As uppity, more Anglicized and far more urbane, us Nairobites were like the N.Y. Yankees — almost professional, talented, and usually exceptional and despised by the other teams. Nairobi was the shining example of freedom and opportunity capable in East Africa and we knew other folks from the smaller, more backward towns envied us. Papa, with his tennis wizardry, was a constant on the Aga Khan team from Nairobi. His presence could almost guarantee AKC Nairobi a win in tennis among the many other sports counting toward overall glory. But at this event, I intended to blaze my own path of popularity. This trip I even met Papa's low expectations of me for I had been selected to represent the club at table tennis. It was a big coming out party and a big deal for me. When I was not playing a match or practicing with zeal, I could parade like a peacock in my finery of faux hand-painted long sleeved shirts and long pants. There would be girls present, daughters of aging athletes or of host club members Mombasa. I was sure they would most certainly appreciate the innate handsomeness of a gawky rake.

The competition for table tennis was to be held on the second of the four day event. Two gleaming tables were the prominent features in the large indoor hall. The nets were perfect and the chairs for spectators were far enough away to allow players ample space to create magnificent shots.

I was determined to win and I had a strategy for this which would have annoyed most folks. I would only play my strongest suit – defense.

Thereby I would force my opponent to be an excellent attacker. I had deduced that most opponents would get increasingly frustrated by my self-professed, startling defensive ability. Unquestionably, I thought that my tactic would cause most opponents to flounder in frustration. I was right.

I breezed easily through my first match and I prepared for my next one. For this second match I was pitted against the best player in the whole tourney. This punk, a fattish slob from some podunk town in Tanzania – Mwanza I think it was - had a band of followers cheering him on, clapping loudly for every point he won. Earlier, I had watched him destroy his previous opponent in straight games, so I knew he was good. My defensive approach would be the only way to get around his faster reflexes and shot making ability.

I got off to a flying start by smothering my opponent with deep defensive chops. This led to a comfortable win in the first of three games. All I had to do now was win one of the next two games to be idolized as the man-boy who won table tennis for Nairobi. I had victory in my sight as I led 15 – 7 in the second game. Only six more points to victory and adulation; perhaps even a girl might be watching.

I was serving, the advantage was mine and I could close this match out. The group directly in front of me, a bunch of cheerleaders for my opponent, was aghast. The pre-tourney favorite was going to go down in flames and this would cripple their chances for winning the overall competition. In my mind the enormity of their loss (and my win) was as big as an elephant turd.

Then, just before I launched my serve, a beefy, unkempt guy in the front row with the demeanor of an ogre, shouted out, "You are a skinny brute."

These five words had the effect of turning my legs to putty and I couldn't move from embarrassment. Things became deathly quiet. The entire weight of the world focused on my shorts, from which stuck out legs that looked more like pencil-thin crutches than things that had muscles. My embarrassment was real, and my heart pounded. My opponent sensed something wrong and he took quick advantage. In a space of a few minutes, I lost the second game. Then, in what must have been a flash, I got crushed in the rubber game and any hope of fame I harbored evaporated.

I never recovered from the humiliation. To this day, even in the searing, mucky, heat of August, I prefer to hide my legs with wear long pants.

My next attempt to gain weight came shortly after that sporting debacle. I was determined to attain some muscles and so with all the money I had saved from previous Eids and birthdays, I went to the "Olympic Sports House" in the City and bought a contraption called the "Bullworker" for the princely sum of 300 shillings. The machine was simple. A bit more than a glorified chest expander, the Bullworker was also designed to also strengthen legs. The magazine ad for this simple machine purported an easy path to muscle making. By forcing an exerciser to use both "isotonic" and "isometric" techniques, a daily five minute workout would lead to noticeable new muscle mass in 30 days.

I thought I'd first work on my upper body and arms. More definition there would make my sunken, flat chest appear more hopeful. Work on my legs could wait; it hurt when I did the leg routines. I hadn't heard of that magic mantra yet – "No Pain, no Gain", so what did I know? A good compromise, it seemed, was to initially focus on my chest and arms.

As part of my regimen, I went on a protein diet eating three raw eggs daily at breakfast. I'd crack open the eggs put them into a narrow glass; yolk, floating on yolk, in a sea of phlegm-like albumin. I'd then add salt and plenty of pepper to mask the slither. In one quick fell gulp, gravity carried this down my gullet to friendly stomach enzymes waiting to turn egg-protein into hard muscle.

It took a few weeks of training before I noticed some definition. I would parade in front of the mirror trying to convince myself that there was a noticeable increase in the tiny bumps that were my biceps. It was difficult to be absolutely sure, so I took a flexible tape measure and began daily measurement of the circumference of my biceps. After a couple of months of diligent exercising, the tape measure suggested I had added half an inch. My muscles were rock hard and there was no question that I felt stronger. But I was still emaciated and thought I needed a boost.

In the comics I read, targeted of course to skinny pre-teens and young teens, I saw an ad for *"Super Wate On"*, a magic syrup that could accelerate weight gain. Once more I reached into my stash of savings. I was a great saver, bordering on the miserly, and I bought two bottles of the precious emulsion. With ingredients like L-lysine Hydrochloride, Nicotinamide, Riboflavine Sodium Phosphate, Pyridoxine Hydrochloride, Thiamine Hydrochloride, Calcium Pantothenate, and Ergocalciferol, there was no way I wouldn't become bigger. The truth is, after sucking down two of those big expensive bottles, I may have gained a pound.

I was at wit's end. I couldn't gain weight no matter what I did. Eventually I made my peace with my despondent alter-ego. I convinced myself that all those extra amino acids I was taking were actually making my brain larger. It was the only excuse I could rely on to save me from utter self-disgrace. So I latched on to learning and reading to help my brain make best use of the supplements. Today, I have mixed feelings for remaining a skinny, lanky brute.

Music: Vol. # 1

*T*he Voice of Kenya broadcasted in English on a solitary frequency. Radio shows were varied by hour and one had to tune in at a particular time to listen to what one preferred. I remember Mummy especially liking Cliff Richard and Elvis and I found that I liked them too. I must have been six or seven and we found these crooners on Mummy's favorite show were *Housewives Choice* which came on at 7:15 AM after 15 minutes of news. As the years passed, I knew that *Housewives Choice* was a misnomer. The program was really a compilation of the latest pop hits such as by Donna Summer, Abba, and Stevie Wonder. Why mothers (housewives) would jig to the likes of Boney M, a disco King, I didn't know. But the program continued its time slot, and as we grew older and were driven to school, the tinny car radio allowed us to keep up with the latest in pop music.

I wasn't a music maven. But I knew that the classical pieces from folks with names like Mozart and Beethoven came on for about an hour each day and, for some unknown reason, sounded very much like what we heard in cartoons such as Bugs Bunny and his melody makers. How shameful of them to copy my beloved Bugs! But I especially hated it when the barley palatable classical music was often rudely changed to operas the imperial white folks insisted on having the Voice of Kenya carry. The high-pitched shrieking I could do without; operas, and opera singers, very much sounded like a troop of baboons having a family feud on a rainy day.

I also acquired a taste for the Indian filmi songs that conveniently came on from 1 – 2 PM each weekday. Papa would sit there, in his comfy chair, blowing post lunch smoke rings into the sounds of Mohammed Rafi, Asha Bhosle, Saigal or Lata Mangeshkar. Indian "filmi" music is incredibly romantic and melodic, even if the movies they frame are of the mostly trashy, goonda versus goonda variety. Goondas (thugs), seemed to have made India a welcome refuge. According to Papa, worse than the goondas were film editor offenders who interrupted a love ballad by layering the last verse with a loud bang from a gun aimed at the heroine's beloved uncle. Such random violence was not an infrequent occurrence, but it always stopped the lovers from completing the fine duet. So lunches at home were often filled with visions fueled by music denoting what could go drastically wrong in the world. If it wasn't the girl's mother or uncle getting shot, it was her getting cancer, or having twins separated at birth, or murder accusations that led to long jail times for the innocent.

Even if they hadn't seen the movie Mummy and Papa loved the images the songs would conjure. Now if they *had* seen the movie to which the song belonged, there would be a long discourse on the lessons learned. I loved these discussions on morals that movies prompted with their songs. For one, Pops would be animated, in a decent enough mood and unlikely to pounce on me for whatever minor or major transgressions I may have committed that day.

I didn't know many band names, but I fell unabashedly in love with certain songs, many of which my sister Ferry had forced me to listen on her scratchy portable radio. I found that I really liked mellow love songs such as "Me and You and a Dog named Boo," and "Puppy Love" by the Osmonds. More importantly, having an older sister was akin to having a guide to help one navigate the morass of confusing radio music. Later on, I found out that the Saturday edition of the *Daily Nation* had a list of the week's top ten pop songs. I would memorize this list, and so claim to be a knowledgeable music lover. It gave me a temporary feeling of being valued in the middle-field with the more mature kids too lazy to read. The pretense I made of knowing the music scene eventually forced me to listen to some of the songs. After all I couldn't pontificate on a song's merit without having listened to it. So with Shainoor's help I got to know a bit about hot performers like Stevie Wonder, Santana, the Jackson Five and Deep Purple.

Shainoor was a year older than me and lived next door with an older brother Farid. When I was about 10 the brothers quietly acquired an actual phonograph with a hi-fi system and stereo speakers. Everyone liked these two exceptionally well-mannered and kind kids who went to the high end, mostly white Hospital Hill primary school. For being such exemplary specimens of children, their parents showered them with lots of gifts and even pocket money. With this they bought complete music albums which amazingly held more than ten songs. Albums were also really mesmerizing because they sported the coolest cover art on them. Only years later did I understand that many of these illustrations were direct appeals to the acid set.

Some of the albums I didn't get. One particular band that made no sense to me was a Ghanaian group called Osibisa that had made it big in England. The group fashioned a type of music called Osibirock sung in Ashanti or some other West African language. We had trouble with our own multitude of Kenyan tribal dialects such as Kikuyu, Mkamba, Kalenjin, and Jaluo. So why would I would turn west to Ghana to understand more of impenetrable Africa? I posed this question to Shainoor, who replied adamantly that Osibisa had the best sound among African bands. From then on I didn't really care to follow the lyrics of most songs. All I was looking for was the beat and melody.

Out of the fountain of my early youth sprang my adoration of Santana. Some of the guitar riffs on their albums were exceptional but I had little compunction of my own to play strings. Learning how to understand and play music was something I never pursued. Most of the aspiring young musicians I saw in teen magazines were dressed in cheap, shoddy clothes, had unkempt hair, and seemed to carry on as exceptional layabouts. There was absolutely no need to fill my mind with musical notes and how to manipulate a set of silly strings when I could easily fill it with stupid facts.

But I did like percussion and being partially reared on Hindi songs, I gravitated to the tabla at an early age. I could play along to certain songs, imitating the beat on our Formica clad mahogany table, which had an interesting resonance with my palms and fingers. I actually got pretty good at mimicking key pieces of percussion in popular songs. Inevitably, however, I would wrongly amplify the tabla's importance and freak out in a fit of unabashed joy, trying to elicit sound from every plate, container, or solid object.

These animated displays would drive Papa nuts, especially when I ruined the elegance of a favorite song with my nonsensical, but determined table thudding. Mummy would come to the rescue, by glaring at Papa, or telling him outright that I was developing a musical talent and that I shouldn't interfere.

It was nice to have my mother as a proponent of my musical talent. So when she asked if I wanted to take tabla lessons, I jumped at the offer. We went to a tabla master's place in upper Parklands to take a look-see. The teacher was an old Sikh with a very white long beard, like Gandalf's. He smiled as we came in and then instructed my mother and me to sit. Mummy explained that I had some talent and that it needed to be nurtured.

The Sikh Guru of Tabla (SGT) looked at me. He saw a nervous boy who fidgeted and looked away. He said, in guttural, heavily singsong English that even my Grandmother would appreciate, "Look now. Chokra. I won't eat you."

I smiled nervously.

"Now see here boy," he continued in Punjabi... I didn't understand the rest because it was in Punjabi. But the words for see and boy in Punjabi are similar to Hindi so I knew he was addressing me.

Anyway Gandalf Singh (SGT) went on a silly rant, looking at me every fifth word, and I knew I was being ushered into a den of discipline. Mummy, who understood Punjabi was nodding her eyes in respect. Clearly we were in the presence of some sage. Then Mummy asked a question in Punjabi, and off they went to some strange place where the truly meditative hang out.

Boy, was this boring and so unfunny. And to think I would be missing *The Flintstones,* which appeared each day at 5:30 PM. What was I thinking? Did I really want to be holed up for two hours each day with an old guy who didn't speak English?

So tabla lessons quickly became a non-starter. Mummy must have been disappointed, but she didn't show it. She was simply a mixture of love and genius.

When I hit the age of 12, I realized that my sister Ferry was a really cool chick and I looked up to her to explain music and the confusing rituals of girls; a breed of humans that I then thought ought to be locked away in far-away castles until they are ripe enough to be mothers. Of course I wasn't much use to Ferry and for much of my childhood Ferry tolerated me like an annoying fly.

Ferry knew far more about life and its emerging wonders, so I was no help there. I didn't know much about the desires of older boys, creatures she was particularly fond of ignoring and then secretly admiring. I couldn't be her protector. Ferry was much bigger than me and her easily ignited temper was often unleashed on circumstances forced upon her by stupid boys. But I was too much of scaredy-cat to display any chivalry. If she was teased by someone, I simply couldn't protect her honor. The paltry meat on my bones wasn't enough to take a single blow, less a barrage from one of the bigger boys who I feared could rip me apart like a tasty chicken drumstick.

Ferry fell in love with Abba and the Carpenters, but this was much later when I was 14. When a troop of us kids sat around the steps leading to the middle field we discussed music at length. "Fernando" was a huge hit, as was "Money, Money, Money" and "Mama Mia". When Amin Kurji, our next door neighbor in Flat #47 and as skinny as me, pointed out that all Abba songs were hokey and sounded alike I came to my sister's defense. I told Amin in a rather unnecessary loud voice that he didn't know what he was talking about. From that moment on, I have been an Abba fan, and Kurji, that skinny shit, and I never again saw eye to eye. He eventually went off to Scotland to study or eat haggis. Whatever, he wasn't that important in my scheme of things and I was glad to have defended my sister, a notable first for me.

By the time I was eight cassette recorders were taking firm hold in Nairobi. For her birthday, Papa bought Mummy a small Phillips version which ran on batteries and could easily be carried from room to room. The music was in mono, but, hey, it was music, and our ears easily adjusted to the low quality sound. Music was now portable and personal (take that, Apple!), and a constant in our lives. As my beacon and Guru of pop, Ferry used a cassette recorder to make me listen to a bootlegged copy of "When Will I see you Again" by the *Three Degrees*. She did this for about a 100 times in the space of two weeks. But I loved the song on my first hearing, and it gave me some insight into soppy area of love.

There were other songs that Ferry and I wore out together that highlighted our youth. The melody attached to the lyrics of "Seasons in the Sun" was so beautiful that we thought this was about a trip to the beach. Only many years later did I find out it was the story of someone dying of cancer, and saying goodbye to his dearest. Anyway, this became our flagship song on a December holiday in Mombasa beach after Ferry took her EACE or (East African Certificate of Education) exams. Passing this test signified that one had complete the minimum for junior high school graduation, and so this was a big deal. My cousins, Aleem and Aisha, were with us that year, and we stayed at an all-inclusive hotel on the beach rather than in-town at my Grandma's. Also joining the party where Sikander Panjwani and his sister Shireen. The other girls, Aisha and Shireen, were Ferry's classmates, and also were in the delirium of having completed a major educational milestone. Aleem, Sikander and I, all two years junior were sent as male chaperones to ensure that this girl-fest didn't get out of hand.

The girls, all of whom had just turned 16, were ecstatic with their first move into womanhood in a mildly independent spot. The Ismailis in Nairobi were a fairly liberal lot. Unlike other Muslim and Hindu families, Ismaili girls could even mention boys without being immediately sequestered by their parents. Ismaili parents in the early 1970s frowned upon teenage girls talking to boys, but they did not ban it.

Thinking that loud singing on the beach would appeal to a gaggle of young, German, male tourists, the girls led all of us to sing our trip's anthem "Seasons in the Sun." We sang this as the sun rose sending everything into a pink hue. In the late evenings, when the African moon shimmered on the Indian Ocean, and the sand felt so good between our toes, we alternated between singing the song and listening to the disco beats pulsating from a dance patio in the hotel next door. Our warbling didn't land the girls any dates, but it was exciting for us chaperones to view the future through the girls' lens of newly found excitement and yearning.

My first role as chaperone to the volatile, good looking, fun filled Ferry was the evening when Shenaz Virjee threw a dance party on her 14th birthday. The party was in the flats and so only a couple of minutes away on foot. For Ferry to get permission, Papa insisted that I tag along. He also gave me explicit instructions to bring my sister back home by midnight. It was my first dance party and I was thrilled to enter the yet unseen world of hormonal blending.

Most of the partygoers were Ferry's age or older, so I settled into a chair in the corner pretending to groove to the music. Shenaz' brother was the DJ, and he played a lot of the popular songs. When he finally put on "Let It Be" by the Beatles, the lights were turned down, and the couples went into slow dance mode. I promptly went to sleep, and didn't get up until two AM when the party broke. Papa was furious. We were supposed to be at home by midnight, and I had failed in my duty.

I gave him my reason for this violation: "I had some lemonade punch, then they played this nice song by the "Beetles", and this made me go to sleep." By recounting this story, I'm pretty sure John Lennon is smirking in his grave. Papa, of course, wasn't amused. There was a gap of two hours I could not account for and so he grounded Ferry forever. I felt great. I didn't want to be Ferry's minder anyway and this unexpected punishment for my sibling was a bonus.

In those pre-teen days, anything I could do to make Ferry's perfect life miserable was critical to my own well being. She was a loudmouth, highly popular among her friends, a girl, and a favorite of many adult parents. She was also strong and could beat the shit out of me. Her heavy right hand when correctly aimed at my face demonstrated to me that her slapping prowess was equal to Joe Frazier's lethal uppercut. It was clear to me that I need not seek her wrath. But any unfortunate happenstance that befell Ferry, such as this grounding by Papa, a torn set of nylons, a broken lipstick, or the arrival of a new zit on her face was enough to make me light up with glee.

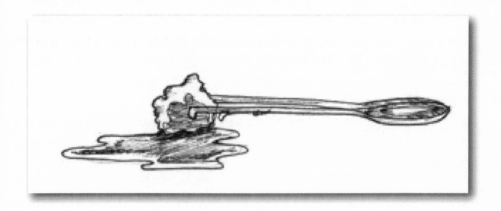

Nicknames

For those who can recall the TV show, Mr. Mooney was the bank manager Lucille Ball forced into a state of constant exasperation. He played his part perfectly, and the woe heaped upon him by Ms. Ball should have driven him to suicide. But then this was a sitcom not reality. The producers knew that keeping Mr. Mooney continuously tortured by the error-prone and hapless Lucy made for excellent comedy.

We had our own Mr. Mooney. Her name was Munira or Muni for short and lived in flat #43, three doors away from us. Our Muni was over-weight, so it could have been easy for callous little boys like us to tease her into own piece of hell. While we were successful in addressing her as Mr. Mooney, her sense of fun turned her into an unlikely hero rather than the butt of our lascivious or cruel jokes. She could do a great dead-pan impression of Mr. Mooney, scowling exactly as he did on the tube when mimicking Lucy or demonstrating one of her antics.

One of the first things we learned from Muni was how to make crank calls. There was a public telephone booth by one of the gates to our compound and Muni had figured how not to pay for calls. By inserting a playing card between the crack of two slabs of steel that housed the phone she was able to trip off a switch that normally would drop only when the right amount of coins fell. With this new found free telephone service we made calls to stockbrokers, taxi services, and butchers pretending to be rich white folk requesting services or products. Since I could mimic the announcers on BBC's shortwave transmissions, I had a decent imitation of a toffish English accent. I was quickly appointed as the person to make the adult-sounding calls. In truth I sounded more like a very young Prince Charles sucking on gobstoppers while reading Chaucer out loud. Among my misdeeds, I ordered phantom rides from Kenatco Taxis fleet of Mercedes and five pounds of fresh prawns to be delivered at precisely noon for an important garden party.

The address for delivery we gave was our own intersection of Masari road, and our compound's gate next to the public pay-phone. These directions were necessarily obscure; we wanted to see if the prank really worked without being nabbed. Over time we had a parade of taxis and delivery trucks run up and down aimlessly at the intersection of Masari road and our compound. When the taxi or delivery van arrived at the designated time, we would burst into unabashed childish laughter. There is nothing funnier to a ten-year-old than making someone else look like a fool. The taxi service figured this out quickly and our trick only worked twice before the taxis stopped coming. The prawns were delivered to no one, but we did see the driver of the "International Fresh Foods" van look a bit peeved.

In addition to Muni, who was merely plump, our flats also boasted a grotesquely obese girl who lived north of the middle-field in flat #6 or #7. Her full nickname was "Duckie Duckie Quack Quack" (DDQQ). She accepted the name Duckie, but not the full DDQQ. I recall being warned about the future use of my balls if I ever called her that. (I think her real name was Shamim, but we always knew her as Duckie).

Duckie's thighs were literally the size of fully grown hams and she waddled around the flats like a pregnant goose. But like Muni she had good cheer and the pair were close friends; two chunkers in slow motion bringing laughter to the young 'uns. Muni and Duckie introduced us to advanced uses of "Black Cat," a licorice-based bubble gum that also had the properties of bonding resin. If planted in one's hair, the gum was impossible to get out unless the offending mess of hair and gum was snipped off close to the skull. One afternoon Muni and Duckie went on exactly such a spree by placing gobs of gum on the heads of unsuspecting kids. They did this in a cruel, sadistic way. First they covered their teeth with the gum, so it appeared they had no teeth, just a gap of black. As inquisitive kids came in closer to see the toothless fat wonders, one of them would surreptitiously place a wad of used gum on the inquisitive person's hair. I was lucky enough to have seen this entire sleight of hand done on Khanbhai, so I was never a recipient. But after Muni's and Duckie's introduction that day, Black Cat become a weapon of choice for all of us kids.

Another of my favorite fat girls was Bessie Bunter. Bessie was a comics character, full of fun and wreaking havoc in her strict English boarding school. We had our own Bessie in our primary school, or at least we nicknamed her Bessie. She may not have had the moxie of Bessie of the comics but at minimum I knew our Bessie as a cake destroyer. I recall perfectly the effortless way she inhaled the icing on a slice of cake at my cousins Daulat's birthday party. It was as if it were a few grams of pure cocaine. Bessie was given her nickname by Daulat's classmates for a specific reason I now fail to recall. But even now I knew the given name was apt. Like the girl in the comic strip, our Bessie had a magnetic smile and the same enlarged thighs and extra large boobs not possible in any other 13-year-old. So the name Bessie stuck.

Bessie was determined to do well at school. I know of this, because many of us kids were hypercompetitive in class. We knew who the best students were a year ahead or behind us. According to my cousin Daulat, Bessie was exceptional at maths. Since she was so fat, however, we cruel boys noted quite pointedly that it was unlikely that a marriage proposal would come her way. Daulat said she was learning maths to become an accountant or smart engineer. I found that a bit confounding. Sure I could understand a woman could be an accountant. Fat tushes were part of the accountants build, or so I thought. But an engineer? Women never became engineers. We had some women doctors, and plenty of teachers, but an engineer? Gosh, I thought then, I had a lot to learn about life.

We also learned to give nicknames from our elders who had applied nicknames to their own childhood friends. Many of these nicknames stuck for decades giving us monikers such as "Baby Soap", Sultan "Tank", or Badru "Passport". Baby Soap was ascribed to my friend Sikander Panjwani's father because his family had once been in the soap business. Panjwani senior hated the term since he was aware of his unpleasant demeanor which, in addition to his rotund middle, made him actually look like a very perturbed Michelin man. But "Baby Soap" stuck, and since nicknames could be passed down to future generations, we called his son Sikander "Soapy" whenever we wanted to make a silly reference to masturbation. This annoyed Panjwani to no end, for we now had the license to crown him "Champion Masturbator" on account of his father's endless supply of soap.

Hamid Hippo was also very appropriately named. He was all of 400 pounds or so and a friend of my mother. If he wore armor, Hamid Hippo could be mistaken for a war machine. But Hamid Hippo actually wore tailor-made suits. We knew this because he had a special pouch to stuff his large "package" that hung low like extra large mangoes and oscillated like a pendulum as he shuffled. Perhaps to incite our wrath, Hamid Hippo, drove a Fiat 600, a car smaller than a VW Beetle, but shaped like a malformed egg. It was a scene to watch a person driving a car that weighed as much as he. For laughs we often found ourselves waiting near his car after evening prayers at the mosque. Watching a man seamlessly transform into a car was a deep, funny spiritual experience for us.

If one wanted travel papers, "Badru Passport" was your man. He had friends in high up places in various parts of the government. With appropriately placed bribes one could get a new, official passport in 48 hours or less. Badru Passport was the community's Mr. Fix-It for all things official and must have kept a large cut of every bribe because he drove a shiny new Mercedes. I never knew his real last name.

Another caustic name given by our parents to one of their cohorts was "Hathi Gando," literally "Mad Elephant" in Gujarati. Why he was mad, we never knew, but when I first saw him, the folds of skin around his neck actually made him look like an elderly pachyderm. I never found him mad, perhaps a little absent minded, but in Kenya if one deviated from the normal Ismaili profile, one was classified evil, or worse yet, insane.

Our parents' parents, that is, folks my granny knew, were also fond of distinguishing their friends with a series of apt monikers. My own grandmother, Fatma, had her surname of Fazal usurped by her friends. She was forever known as "Fatma Topiwari", which literally translated into "Fatma of Hats". Granny's husband (my grandfather) died from tuberculosis when Fatma was about 22. By then she had three kids of her own and one other from my grandfather's previous wife who also had succumbed to an early African death.

The year was 1924. The Nineteenth Amendment to the United States Constitution allowing women to vote had only just been ratified in August 1920, and way before Gloria Steinem's mission for imparting equality between the sexes. Fatma Topiwari, born in Zanzibar, the center of the East African slave trade that lasted until the late 19th century, would have had a very difficult time with few resources and no help from her relatives.

So this exceptionally strong woman took over the foundering business of importing Fez hats her husband had just started in Mombasa. Fatma (Fatu – for short) was the toughest entrepreneurial cookie. While raising four kids she built up the hat business into a tiny empire. She diversified into property and farming, and the name Fatma Topiwari was meant more as a sign of deep respect than a slight.

Fatma loved playing cards (rummy) for small stakes. She was too conservative and smart enough not to develop a really bad gambling habit. But cards were her passion and way to let off steam. Often she would host card "parties" for her friends from the mosque. Her friends had interesting nicknames like "Chuklibai", (Bird Lady). I only knew her as Bird Lady, and with her hooked nose she looked like an overgrown budgie. Many years later I found out that her nickname stemmed from her fancy of exotic birds. Apparently, she kept a few as pets. So once again, my eager brain that excelled at overanalyzing had led to me to false waters.

Another of Fatma's card playing female mates was KenyaFishwari (again literally translated as "of the Kenyafish"). KenyaFishwari's husband ran a fish distribution company. To me, she looked like a predatory shark with her dark, beady eyes and very stern look.

Since my parents, grandparents and even we their children made a habit of assigning nicknames, many of these stuck. As children, parents, and grandparents, meandering in Kenya's comfortable paradise, we sometimes gave nicknames to each other out of love but mostly to tease and insult. With my nickname of Feshu (short for Feisal), I was also the target of lyrical composition. I hated the rhyme "Feshu Deshu Ghand ma che Moti Kisu," which, when translated, noted that I have a big knife stuck up my arse. (Kisu is Swahili for knife). Another nicknames affixed to me was "Harry Worth," after a bumbling British TV comedian. Harry Worth was a silent screen actor who I believe gave eventual rise to the success of that legendary British buffoon, Mr. Bean. I hated that nickname, too. I am also reminded by some that because of my clumsy nature, their favorite nickname of me was "Hot Lips Swindley, yet another comedic TV character in the 1960's BBC show, *Pardon the Expression.* But perhaps the most famous nickname belonged to mother's friend who was given the name Sweet Gum Arabica. Please don't ask why.

American Milkshakes & Hamburgers

Papa got Mummy a Hamilton Beach blender for her 40th birthday. It was the early 1970s and women, especially Indian women, were thrilled to get anything from their husbands. Even vacuum cleaners were appreciated by the legions of women starved for recognition, love and respect. Ferry and I thought what a wonderful gift my father had given. And yes, what a lovely American thing to do. We also loved the name "Hamilton Beach" since it put us right into latitude where we could dream about beaches more pristine than Mombasa's. (An impossibility of course, but then we were kids with unbridled imaginations). I ran outside to boast to friend Khanbhai about our shiny new acquisition and the accompanying 50 page manual that instructed housewives how to make frozen margaritas, mincemeat from steak, and chop onions. My news broadcast likely set of a wave of blender buying in the flats that must have caused a perceptible rise in Hamilton Beach's stock price.

There were five settings on the blender. I can only recall three of these – mix, chop and liquefy. Many years later, after watching *Soylent*

Green, I realized why there was a liquefy setting. Anyway, Mummy decided that the blender would only be used for making milkshakes. She didn't want to have the inside contaminated by the odor of meat or garlic. We saw her point.

But we insisted on it being used immediately. Since we didn't have any ice cream at home – our fridges being too tiny to house frozen concoctions of any sort, save a small ice tray, we did the next best thing. We three kids piled into Mummy's Volkswagen beetle and set off for the suburb of Westlands ten minutes away. Westlands had an ice cream shop that sold an almost perfect vanilla. I knew because I was a vanilla connoisseur. As a kid I never ate any flavor of ice cream except vanilla. I could never understand, and still to this day, don't know why anyone would bastardize ice cream by adding chocolate or, god forbid, strawberry flavoring. When I hit the United States many years later and first went into a Baskin Robbins garishly displaying its 31 flavors, I thought the world had gone mad.

I wanted a large carton of vanilla. Ferry was being difficult and said she wanted to try a chocolate shake. I went into an immediate pout and our caring little sister, Rozy, no more than three, noticing my anguish sided with me. So Mum bought vanilla, after bribing Ferry with yet another dress for an upcoming religious festival.

We went back home and gathered in the kitchen. Papa was sitting in his easy chair sipping an early Sunday beer. Rozy was agog with happiness. I can remember her sitting on the kitchen counter watching Mum be precise with the ingredients; ice cream, whole milk from the Kenya Cooperative Creamery (KCC), and vanilla essence. As Mum started the blender for the first time, we were awed by the power of the motor which made the shake in two seconds flat. All four of us burst into wide grins. This simple concoction was bliss in more ways than one. Papa declined a glass. He was already on his second beer and didn't' want to ruin his nascent buzz.

The love affair with all things American was a constant for us. What a lovely, free, funny, warm yet treacherous world America portrayed on

71

television. While we were natural Anglophiles, having been born in colonial times, reading Enid Blyton, and eating Cadbury's Milk Chocolate,
America had a special but alien place in our psyche. Most, if not all, of
what we knew about America, was through our trusty black and white
television. We watched and fell in love with Dennis the Menace confounding Mr. Wilson, Leave it to Beaver, and the adult favorite, Perry
Mason, which came in at 9:30 PM once a week. We were only allowed to
watch one late evening program a week and by Ferry's decree this was
Perry Mason. . Our entire brood cuddled together with blankets on
the old family couch as we saw Paul Drake, Della Street and that incomparable Mr. Mason break open a case in the cleverest of ways. We felt
bad for the prosecuting attorney, the ever-present but dumb Mr. Burger,
whose pouty lips and bull-in a-china-shop like qualities seemed to give
Mr. Mason a distinct advantage. The murders were always seemed to occur in highly fashionable areas by jealous lovers, many of whom sported
large sexy sunglasses and drove outsized cars with remarkable tail fins.
As Mr. Mason unraveled the murders with the skill of Poirot and the determination of those waiting for Godot, we grew up knowing that crime,
and especially murder, never pays.

Secretly, all of us boys wanted to relive our lives as Dennis the
Menace. His constant haranguing of Mr. Wilson, some deliberate and
some accidental, was boy paradise. In our flats, we had our own version of Mr. Wilson – Jimmy Nurali, who, with his wife and two children
Jenny Wenny, and Ali, lived directly across from our beloved middle-
field. When Jimmy had decided on the house, I bet he never fathomed
the green outside his bedroom window to be the center of important
sporting activity. For our cricket wicket we used a perfectly placed util-
ity pole less than ten yards away. This pole also served as one of four
goal posts when he played football or field hockey. This was great for
us kids, but a total nightmare for Jimmy, who loved his weekend siestas.
We exasperated him constantly by shouting at the top of our lungs, ex-
horting our teammate to pass the ball or expressing the joy in a fallen
wicket. We weren't doing this on purpose; we were just boys being boys.

After enough disturbing screams of "Howzat's" one Saturday afternoon, Jimmy came down and gave us a scolding. He wasn't very nice, just very threatening. He let us know in no uncertain terms that he would confiscate our bats and ball. He must have had a bad day, hangover or something, for his eyes were beetroot red and sweat had stained the armpits of his pajama top.

Lalji, the most brave and belligerent of our group spoke up, "That's stealing. Besides, we are not on your property." Jimmy, not expecting a remark from a snot-nosed kid, blew his top. He seized the bat Virani was holding and stormed off.

What a silly ass! Did Jimmy Nurali think we were not going to retaliate? Emboldened by Lalji's bravado, we immediately took it upon ourselves to aggravate Jimmy. We found another bat and took turns batting, trying to hit his window conveniently positioned at square leg. It took all of three deliveries for Virani to shatter the corner of a window with a well placed strike. We heard Jimmy scream from inside his house. But we weren't yet men enough to confront him again so we bolted, giggling at our successful terrorist act. We promised ourselves we would never admit who broke the window. We surmised that a window can break only once, so how could five boys "collectively" break one window? We thought that was genius thinking on our part. As long as everyone denied breaking the window, each one of us was safe.

Jimmy ended up visiting all our parents seeking answers to the crime. We were steadfast having earlier sworn to each other to never implicate each other. All we answered was, "It wasn't me." When pressed by Jimmy in front of our parents, we all lied brilliantly and each of us said, "I don't know". It was a boldfaced lie, but each of us now had gained a lesson in solidarity and comradeship. Boy, were we proud of ourselves.

Unsuccessful at questioning us in front of our parents, Jimmy tried to have the police press us to confess. A few days after our victory, Jimmy strode confidently towards our group in the middle field. He was accompanied, by a big African chap wearing the traditional khaki of the police. Jimmy introduced the African chap as an inspector with the

Criminal Investigation Department (The Kenyan version of the FBI). By now we realized we were in a full scale war. Messing with the police could be dangerous and our legs began to turn into jelly. But Lalji, having seen too many B movies at Shan Cinema in Ngara, brazenly asked the man for his police ID. Of course the imposter didn't have one. So we, a group of young urchins, had shamed Jimmy once more. Jimmy never bothered us after that, and all of us had learned a core tenet of being American – which is to always "Question Authority". We had made Mark Twain proud.

Cartoons on TV were another solid vehicle for understanding the American psyche. From our experiences with Popeye and Olive Oyl, we kids recognized that hamburgers were an exalted American food, and therefore a fine example of haute cuisine. We also knew from those who had travelled abroad, that the best place to get a burger was at a genuine American joint. Unfortunately, this being Africa of the early 1970s meant there weren't any McDonalds, Burger Chef or Burger King outlets. The closest thing we had was a Wimpy's, a British-based franchise where the burgers were fashioned in the American style. Or at least that's what how we convinced ourselves to love the cheap fried meat. And this being deep dark Africa, there was only one Wimpy outlet in all of Nairobi. But it was good enough for us.

The Wimpy bun was soft and perfectly browned on the outside. First, the grill chef with his silly hat sautéed onions and meat in some kind of foreign grease. He then plopped a burger patty on to the bun and topped it off with the onions. There was no magic sauce like in a Big Mac, so, save for the fat drippings, we piled on the Ketchup. There was an abundance of this stuff at Wimpy's. We were fully aware that eating Ketchup was an all American right and we all became addicted to the tangy red sauce. We didn't have the famous Heinz brand in Kenya, but we made do with the local Peptang, concocted in an industrial area near the Embakasi airport.

There were also a couple of pseudo American Restaurants in Nairobi. Most of these were run by the same Ismaili family, who targeted our parents and us with mouth-watering recipes of Chicken Tikka Masala burgers and milkshakes in tall glasses. One restaurant was called *Exotica* and sat directly opposite a large municipal parking lot. This was quite a good thing for older kids with access to their parents' cars. On Friday evenings after Mosque, they would gather in the lot to gossip, ogle at girls and be served the delicious fast food by African waiters in sneakers. It was a far cry from the American ideal –being catered to by pretty young blond teenagers, with supple breasts, and on roller skates. (With this image stuck to our brains, we could only surmise that all Americans had really died and simply gone to heaven).

But we, too, were happy in the cool Nairobi air, sipping vanilla milkshakes, eating a plate of masala fries or that classic Arabic bread mixed with seasoned mincemeat and egg. Exotica also had a full-scale charcoal grill where they roasted spicy meats. The chicken pieces were succulent and tender and the shish kabobs were exquisite.

This didn't go unnoticed by our Hindu friends whose mothers only cooked vegetarian food at home. Often one would see throngs of wealthy Shahs and Patels congregating in an armada of fancy cars to savor the delightful morsel of forbidden meat.

For us young Ismailis, this was proof that Muslims were better people than Hindus. Meat eating after all was a Muslim's birthright. By eating meat the normally veggie Hindus were affirming our religious superiority. Of course this logic didn't count in reverse since many Ismailis were lushes, drinking the forbidden elixir of scotch whiskeys or Tusker lager. Are wine-swilling Christians better than us Ismailis? Of course not! It was precisely this kind of banal thinking that has led us to so many wars. So as I write this today I am grateful for America, where there truly is a separation of church and State and the accompanying freedom to believe in loud Pentecostal ministers, ancient rocks, the proud buffalo, or nothing at all.

Cartoons

Cartoons were like rice or bread, a necessary staple for living. My love affair with cartoons began when I was about four. Instead of taking my regular afternoon nap, as ordered by the master of the universe who went by the name of Papa, I went downstairs and switched on the telly to watch Mighty Mouse. I felt an immediate kinship to this tiny rodent whose unspoken role was to be protector of the earth and to save us briefly from our destinies. The mouse's small size mirrored my own vulnerability especially in the face of angry beast Papa.

Even at this modest age, I thought I could get around Papa's rule. Papa usually terrified me but it was Mighty Mouse that held my spell that day, and I was compelled to watch. But Papa came in early from work that day and caught me red-handed, my eyes fully glued to the screen. I felt a wave of pain approaching rapidly. The only possible recourse from a horrible sentence was to have Mummy shield me; but Mummy was upstairs taking a nap, supposedly with me by her side. So I braced for impact or death and I got it in the form of my first scolding. Papa, this guy who would rarely smile at me but shower his love and handsome smile at my evil sister, was wildly successful at inducing guilt. This first lecture was clearly worse than any kind of thrashing or torture and for a young tyke seemed to last an eternity. (Papa only physically struck at me once when I was eight, but that's another story).

I was told to sit down and reminded laboriously on why kids need naps and other correct behaviors to turn into good little boys. Papa clearly pointed out several times, like a prosecutor refining his argument, that I wasn't a good little boy. At my tender age Pop's outrage really meant I was a miserable piece of shit, that someone should beat the living crap out of me and then murder my beloved mother and protector. After being excoriated for what seemed like decades, Mummy came down to find me whimpering. She put her arms around me, then smiled warmly at Papa and the merciless scolding came to an end. All was well again.

Another childhood favorite cartoon of mine was Popeye the Sailorman the spinach-fortified hero. After only a couple of electric episodes of Popeye, I too went on a spinach eating binge. But like an anorexic, I would reject this green vile as unsuitable for my stomach. The only difference was I'd poop rather than throw up after eating. Mummy adored my new found interest in leafy greens and she prepared the stuff for me in several ways, all which tasted the same - horrid and slimy. But I was determined to get some Popeye-styled muscles, and the spinachfest continued until Papa complained loudly about the lack of variety in the family menu. To this day I still largely blame him for rendering me into a skinny weakling. If only I had stayed on a spinach diet.

Always disconcerting to me about Popeye's character was his fascination with Olive Oyl. Here was this amazing sailor who was funny, kind, defender of the free world, smoked an adorable pipe and all he could land was this whiny, complaining bitch? I always have thought a lady like that would lead to a man's downfall, but I let it slide because Popeye always got the better of mean Brutus.

There were so many cartoons we treasured, many heightened by the communal viewing that occurred between 5:30 and 6 PM. This was the slot the Voice of Kenya (VoK) had allocated to us kids. After the show most of us who had been watching in our respective flats, would rush out to recount and celebrate the banalities, foibles or victories performed by the animated heroes or dolts. Meeting up was a bit tricky to accomplish, because prayers at the mosque started at 6:30, barely leaving enough time to splash water on the face and put on a clean shirt and a pair of socks. But we often managed. Each of us kids had our favorites but I think if we had a well-monitored vote, the Flintstones would win for best ever. We all wanted to be strong like Bam-Bam, and Pebbles was the cutest girl in the world. Fred was a likable sort despite his many faults, and Barney and Betty were the model couple, always so attentive and sympathetic to each other. Wilma, Fred's wife, was a lovely lady and saint who found it in her to love and cherish the exasperating ways of her boisterous Fred.

With his overly clever (or just plain dumb) schemes, Fred would inevitably get Barney and himself into some kind of morass with the fuzz, his boss or with their wives. The crux of many episodes was devoted to capers needed to extricate Fred and Barney from one of Fred's loopy ideas. But what we enjoyed most were the modern contraptions designed for the Stone Age. For example, to shave, Fred plopped a bee in a cup and placed it against his jaw. Now firmly caught and but trying noisily to escape, the annoyed bee would buzz his way through Fred's stubble exactly like an electric Remington or Philishave.

The needle for the Flintstones record player came courtesy of a peculiar bird whose sole purpose was to point its very sharp beak on to revolving plate fueled by a rabid hamster in a wheel. We noticed as kids, that many of Bedrock-era household appliances were created by animals. Some of these bedraggled overworked creatures also had cameo roles, uttering classic one-liners depicting their woe of being enslaved for the sake of modern convenience. Even in those days of unbridled optimism that were the 1960s, we were taught that luxury or convenience came at a price.

I especially could resonate with the way Fred Flintstone would start his car by first running to get the engine to tick over. This particular method of igniting the engine was so realistic for Kenya where batteries often went dead from overuse or faulty wiring. It was quite a frequent sight to see drivers with one hand on the wheel, pushing their cars down a slope to jump start the engine, before diving back in to maintain control.

Another of our favorite cartoon show's was based on the adventures of two reptiles known as the Tijuana Toads called Pancho and Toro. This was a well-loved, but short lived series about the adventures of the two Mexican frogs trying not to get squished or eaten as they foraged for food. Both had incredibly long tongues to nab lunch that posed as a fly or some other buzzing insect. Our first Spanish language lessons also came courtesy of the frogs. Before the arrival of this pair of hobo like amphibians with a delightful sense of humor, I hadn't ever heard spoken Spanish. Even then, all I could understand that "si" meant "yes". The cartoon put into perspective for us, that Mexico was a hot country, with lots of cactus, plenty of time for siestas, and the principal supplier of that mellifluous language that is now affectionately termed Spanglish.

We Indian kids had an especially proud feeling when *Johnny Quest* appeared. Johnny, with his sidekick Hadji, the son of a wealthy Indian maharajah, ended up on crazily exciting adventures, many of which likely served as the model for the Indiana Jones series of movies. I'm pretty sure Steven Spielberg had to have been a Johnny Quest fan. Hadji, the turbaned Indian prince, was our hero for we finally knew then that there was room for fame and fortune for little brown boys. The exhortation and admiration of us by all our elders could not have had the same effect on us as Hadji on Johnny Quest did.

When I reached the United States to begin college, I was quickly indoctrinated into TV shows that were not privy to us Kenyans when growing up. One of my new favorites became the stories of Mr. Ed, the irascible but funny talking horse owned by a guy called Wilbur. Prior to Mr. Ed, however, I had seen a talking horse as the lead for a cartoon series. Quick Draw McGraw was a horse and peacekeeper of a mythical town in the Wild West. He was drawn replete with a Sheriffs badge, two six guns, a twelve gallon hat and a saddle. We always wondered about the saddle, because no one actually rode on Quick Draw. In fact much of the time I recall him running around upright on two legs shooting away at bad guys. This kind of clever fantasy drew us even more to America where even horses were free and funny. It was a far cry from Kenya's angry lions, marauding hyenas, and vicious crocodiles. We imagined America's wildlife to be an amalgam of happy bears like Yogi and Boo-Boo, dastardly park rangers with nothing better to do than harass these adorable bears, and stupid coyotes getting constantly outwitted by the Road Runner.

For a while we also believed everything good and new came from an American company called Acme. Acme was the ubiquitous brand for advanced technology such as bridge-building kits, flying machines, and extra strong dynamite, all of which were exquisitely demonstrated in episodes of the *Road Runner*. Despite this technological prowess that only Wile E. Coyote seemed to possess, the enigmatic Road Runner always eluded the deathly charms and traps of the crazy canine. It was common for us boys to go around the flats in a chorus of "Beep-Beeps" as a secret taunt to some of the older bullies in the flats. For, in the end, we knew we would win: we had the power of the almighty "Beep-Beep".

It is rare that a cartoon series produces two characters both of which perfectly reflect one's psyche if not character. The glorious *Pink Panther* did both. An ex-girlfriend said I reminded her of the spindly, gangly, conniving feline. In particular she noted that I had the exact same lazy gait and vacant look whenever we went for a stroll. At first I was upset to be compared to this strange, skinny cat. I still looked very much like a stick insect and didn't need my girlfriend telling me that I walked and looked like a wimp as well. Eventually I took this as a compliment because I could imitate the Panther's gestures with reasonable accuracy.

This got me a few laughs from my buddies and an occasional kiss from the normally cold-as-ice girlfriend. The Pink Panther was also unassumingly clever. Admittedly, he was a kind of a goof, but by studiously examining the ways he thwarted his nemesis, "Inspector Clouseau," I vastly increased my capabilities for cunning.

The second character trait, also borne out of panther-related antics, was affixed to me by my cousin Abeed. We had just watched the movie *Return of the Pink Panther* at the Kenya Cinema, when he turned squarely to me in our balcony seats and said. "You are the inspector." My face turned red and I was grateful that the lights were still dim. Clouseau was a funny, bumbling, clumsy detective who somehow with incredible luck got it right and nabbed the thief. But if there ever was an illustration of a moronic, error-prone fool in a dictionary, it would clearly have a picture of Clouseau.

At dinner later that evening, Abeed announced to everyone that I was the perfect incarnation of Clouseau. When even my very own mother who had seen the movie produced a big smile, in effect confirming Abeed's thesis, the nickname of Clouseau stuck. I hated Abeed for that because I felt quite silly being compared to this maniac whose French was perfectly accented with English. In the end it was a close shave, for my antagonist, Abeed, lived in Mombasa and couldn't spread his findings to my Nairobi friends. But whenever we went to Mombasa on vacation, Abeed would address me as "Inspector" reminding me that clumsiness, genius at being accident prone, and my often downright stupidity were constant pillars of my behavior.

Completing this contemplation on cartoons without mentioning Disney or Bugs Bunny would be blasphemous to the legions of artists who made kids lives meaningful. I am not sure I could survive the wrath of Mickey or the "fuwwy wittle wabbit" if they were to meet me at the gates of hell. For the most part, I thought the Disney cartoons were simplistic and silly. They had no charm and very little bite. These harmless animated sojourns were bland like ketchup without tomatoes or salt and never induced a guffaw from me. Unlike Bugs I never saw Donald Duck face multiple threats to death, and whatever was the use of Goofy? Not only was Goofy a moron, but he had no redeeming value. He was simply the dumbest of animals and spent most of his time as annoying wallpaper for other silly Disney characters.

Consider that Disney's Mickey Mouse wasn't as cool as Mighty Mouse, even half as quick or appealing as Speedy Gonzalez, and nowhere was he as clever as the Jerry of *Tom and Jerry*. Mickey had this cheesy vacant grin wherever he went that made me want to punch him. I grant that Mickey may have scored a real babe in Minnie Mouse, but then I'm sure that was some artist's personal fantasy. Besides every boy under the age of 13 thought Minnie Mouse as a shrill, domineering little bitch and an unwelcome sight – the pre-teen equivalent of Martha Stewart and her 100 ways to drive one's husband nuts. Why would anyone want to be tortured so?

I grant that Disney's magic with full length animated films is somewhat compelling. But the Disney stuff we saw on TV was just mush. The true lure of Disney, was, of course, Disneyland, a paradise for kids. It was where every kid wanted to die and go to heaven. I realize that we were several thousand miles away from Florida or Anaheim, but we could still dream. But getting a ride in an oversized teacup, or saying hello to a life-size Mickey was not educational and inspiring. Disney characters, it must be said loudly for all to hear, were nincompoops.

To compensate for Mickey's mediocrity, there was Bugs and his accompanying army of brilliant *Looney Tunes* characters such as Yosemite Sam and Elmer Fudd, all of whom were surreal and mesmerizing. It was Bugs who excelled at everything and especially at torture. I loved Bugs, and he was the best role model. I hope you agree that he dominates the cartoon hall of fame like Pele, Babe Ruth, Gretzky, and Lew Alcindor do in their respective sports.

Black Tablets

Sikander Panjwani was the kind of guy who would tell you, *after* you spent the princely sum of 20 shillings for a haircut and blow-dry, that your previous haircut was so much better. Panjwani's bitterness was trying and downright annoying. But we boys put up with him, because his family provided us with so much fodder for ridicule. Panjwani's father was known as Sabu or "Soap", a nickname he hated, at least that's what our parents told us. To us, Panjwani Senior was a hard driving robot with the sole mission of becoming immensely wealthy. He owned a shop for selling car parts and, as claimed by Sikander, it was the best stocked parts store in the city. We couldn't argue with this boast since most of didn't know a sparkplug from a distributor cap. But we felt it was highly pedantic of Sikander to incessantly remind us of the many different types of hubcaps his father stocked in the "gold mine" called his father's shop.

Sikander moved in with his family from Kisumu in Western Kenya one Saturday morning when I was about eight. Our regular crew of

Aloo, Khanbhai, Virani, Lalji and I gathered around like hyenas smelling fresh meat. Sikander's family set up home in a flat right next to our beloved middle field. This allowed us immediate and ample insight into this new family's make-up.

When we saw the father gruffly telling his kids to move the boxes carefully we knew we would make fun of this alien family from the hinterland. First off, who would possibly want to have been born in the backwardness of the land that sat next to mosquito ridden Lake Victoria? We knew this new boy Sikander was second rate as soon as we found out that Kisumu was his former home. We kids knew that most of Kenya's imbeciles were bred near the lake or elsewhere despicably rural, say in desolate Turkana province or near Lamu. To prove our point we noticed over the next few days that Sikander's command of the language was worse than mediocre. He mixed metaphors, butchered grammar and pronounced some words like the country bumpkin that he was. With the added ignominy of not knowing the meaning of phrases such as "What's up, Doc", or "Silly Wabbit," he was a veal calf awaiting slaughter. Kisumu didn't have television then or at least that what we surmised. Panjwani's utter lack of knowledge of anything related to the true window into our hearts and minds – the television – was so glaring, that either he was an imbecile or deprived.

It turned out the latter was true. Panjwani's father saw no use for a TV and never said a word to us or had a kind smile. He was focused on making money, and lots of it. An image I have of him, that still infuses a smile today, is of his sparklingly efficient waddle. With a nice round belly, a perfectly flat ass and a scowl that could scare crows, we got to admire his determination as he plodded with precision up the short set of steps from his flat to his beloved car. As kids in love with all things car, we envied and admired the sporty, banana-yellow Toyota 2000.

Panjwani Senior (Sabu), was a little Napoleonic prick who, like most short little pricks, thought that the size of one's penis was directly related to the way one drove a car. It wasn't any car that one could drive for this purpose. It had to be sporty and eye-catching. There was no question that his yellow Toyota 2000 made the grade. Panjwani senior would rev up the engine and burn rubber like he was a Malay king. We thought he was a complete flake, and we dropped many overt hints to Sikander, that his father was a loser with a serious complex.

After all, how many bald guys in their late 30's would want to be chick magnets and drive fast cars to prove their manhood? Many years later I realized that was actually a genetic defect present in many males, including Panjwani senior. It led me to a question: Why do girls torment us so?

Well Panjwani senior, more than met his match in his wife. Panjwani's mum was kind of a looker, and her very wide hips denoted her ability to make strong babies. On her pretty face she would regularly make the drastic mistake of applying a ton of make-up giving her the look of an angry porcelain doll. We joked that a fire truck would be needed to hose down her face prior to sleeping. Perhaps she thought that that white plaster on an otherwise brown face was becoming. While many Africans and Indians wanted to display light complexions under Kenya's hot sun, this did not suit Panjwani's mum. Looking like a caked-up Geisha re-plete with anger furrows an inch thick she accentuated what we kids thought was her mean and cruel spirit. Whenever she emerged so, we noted quite cunningly that "Warpaint" was on the "warpath". And in battle mode she always seemed to be.

She had a loud guttural voice reminiscent of those nasty German colonels we saw in movies and used her decibels to very good measure. The recipient of many of these blood-curdling screams was son Sikander. Apparently Sikander could do nothing right. His sister, Shireen, on the other hand, had a brilliant mind and led her pack of cohorts in all things academic. But it didn't stop there. Shireen was pretty, an athlete and dominated netball and rounders, the two school funded girl sports. So to his mum, Sikander was the ultimate shit-for-brains who could do nothing right. Sikander was an especially poor student and likely made even worse from the incessant scolding his mother gave him. At exam time he became a withering mess. His results showed an utter lack of confidence and an obvious thick skull, as both my cousin Aleem and I consistently crushed him in every subject. This didn't go over too well in the highly competitive Panjwani household, where sister Shireen could do no wrong.

It was only inevitable that Panjwani was the primary recipient of his mother's wrath. Our favorite line that she screamed in her broken, incorrect English was: *"Sikander! What nonsense talking you!"*

Since their flat was dead smack next to middle-field where us kids congregated, this constant humiliation of Sikander was a much desired spectacle. We would purposely sit outside waiting for his mother her to come back from shopping or mosque so that we might get a glimpse of any new torture Sikander might have to endure. The feeling was like being at the coliseum watching a hopeless slave chained at the feet fighting off a pack of starving lions. Whenever we heard that Nazi-like scream, we knew Sikander was in big doo-doo.

One time Mum Panjwani was so angered that first she screamed and then raced into the middle field to find her son. He was, of course, sitting next to us kids. Sikander got up ever so reluctantly and went to meet his mother; his head hung low to avert the fury in her eyes. When they met, at the gutter that separated middle field from the patch of grass near his house, she pulled Sikander's chin up, and gave him the most resounding strike across the face. Then, like an expert swordsman, she backhanded him with another strike. Only a practiced and expert punisher could have meted out this effective one-two. But Mum Panjwani wasn't done yet. She pulled at his Sikander's hair with a deep vengeance and dragged him indoors.

In contrast to Sikander, Panjwani's mum gave her youngest son, Asif, who was only about four or five, a free pass to terrorize and create havoc. Asif was a lovable, cute little tike with a constant grin on his face. He had muscled legs and could run like the wind. I envied his well formed physique and for a moment or two I wished his mother had borne me. But this was silly; I wouldn't trade my mother for anything. Sister Ferry could perhaps be exchanged for someone who was less of a bully and show-off, and Rozy my little adorably cute sister I could absolutely not give up. Papa was without question eminently tradable for someone who simply wouldn't glare down and scold me for the tiniest of violations.

Many years later as I was exposed to drugs such as mescaline, magic mushrooms and weed, I realized why some little kids like Asif were bonkers. A theory I still hold is that all kids are born with a huge reservoir of LSD that, over time, slowly dissipates like a radioactive material. At birth this LSD floods into the brain, and all that the baby can do is drink milk, party all night, poop, have nightmares and cry, and then blessedly go to sleep. This process is repeated for the first six months, at which point the LSD dose is lessened, and the kids become veritable smiling puff dolls with the odd outburst from a bad trip. By the time they get to Asif's age they are overtly rambunctious and see the world as one big oyster. Moreover, I am of the impression that Asif's built-in supply of LSD was of the extra strong variety. And to extend my hypothesis, I believe that if free reign is given to such kids, it is like overfeeding them on extra strong blotters. So in short we had a complete maniac and monster on our hands who gave us immense amounts of pleasure watching his antics.

Asif, at the tender age of four, used his already well defined physique to scale low trees for weaver bird nests. He would then bring the eggs back home and throw them against his house wall to create a delightful Rorschach effect. Another of his practice sessions of utter cruelty dealt with small lizards. Asif would capture a platoon of these small cute little crocodile "wanna-be's" and put them in a closed box. He would then get out his mother's kitchen shears and chop off their tails. His work complete, he would release them back, one by one, into the wild of the middle-field. The stuff he did with spiders and grasshoppers is unmentionable.

Panjwani Senior (Shabu) also had a special place in his heart for his tiny tyke. On several occasions we saw Asif sitting on his father's lap in the sporty Toyota *actually* controlling the wheel. This was further proof to us kids that cute little boys like Asif, handpicked by the devil to inflict terror, were repaid for misgivings by being allowed to do exactly what they wanted. Life wasn't fair, and for our friend Sikander, the outcast of his own family, it was fraught with misery.

What could you say about a guy who was forced by his mother to take five black capsules a day to improve his memory? Apparently these pills contained enough essence of almond purported to enhance fact retention such as multiplication tables, key dates of Julius Caesar's reign and the nuances of English grammar. To us it wasn't the oddity of taking capsules – my mother for example favored to give us a daily capsule of cod liver oil. But the way Sikander's mum insisted on his taking these black capsules would incite a riot of laughter among us kids. To explain, black in Gujarati translates as "kari" and capsule is "golli". Yet in Kenya another derogatory term for a black woman was "golli", adopted from the white settlers' frequent use of the word golliwog. In effect, Sikander's mum made sure her son did not evade swallowing his memory boosters by screaming in Gujarati, "Sikander... have you taken your five kari gollis?"

For a while, Aloo and I made it habit of hanging out outside the Panjwani windows, waiting for these words that sent us into fits of laughter. See, we translated her almost desperate but angry plea as an unwavering commitment to Sikander's need for a daily regimen of *five black women.*

As far as odd parents go, Sikander's dad came in a close second to his wildly entertaining mum. We grasped the range of Panjwani's senior's idiosyncrasies when one Sunday afternoon he rushed out in his pajamas to confront some dastardly perpetrators. One of us, again most likely our fearless Lalji, had the brilliant idea to feed his son Sikander a rumor that a handful of the older flat boys were stealing hubcaps during Sunday's siesta time.

We had learned from Sikander that for some unfathomable reason, his dad's Toyota could not keep its hubcaps on. The car had the annoying habit of regularly losing one or more of its shiny silver wheel covers. This puzzled Panjwani junior but irked senior to no end. So we fed

Sikander the lie that the older boys would then take their loot on #12 bus to the broad, wide corner where Parklands ended and Ngara began. Here they would exchange their silver for cigarettes.

Our fabrication was entirely believable since the corner actually existed and was a local spot to hawk or fence items. The "corner" had adequate space for ten illegally parked cars and was especially good for greens and fruit. The vegetarian Hindus who had made Ngara their home were natural magnets for the farmer - hawkers trekking in daily from Limuru and other rural areas of Nairobi to sell their fresh produce. Next to the fruit stalls were "metal" vendors who sold glittery spare parts including, hub caps. Our lie fit much better than O.J.'s glove.

When we laid the trap we knew that Panjwani junior, so very eager to be on the right side of his parents, would immediately inform senior. There were always extra points for a boy when your father approved of you. To us, apart from Panjwani's mum, every other mother had the natural instinct to mollify their little "chokra's" daily deeds. But for fathers' to praise their sons, meant one had done something really worthy.

Using old paint lids we could simulate the effect of hubcaps falling on tarmac or concrete. On this particular Sunday we let paint lids clang loudly to the cement. This leads up us to the point in our story of flapping balls and a hairy butt-crack.

Hearing a metal racket, Panjwani senior, his balls swishing and hairy ass-crack clearly perceptible, flew out of his house and ran up the short steps to his parked car. With his eyes blazing in anticipation at getting at the thieving marauders he leapt on to the scene like some madman in his cotton pajamas too thin to mask his nuts knocking and a cheap fulana (undershirt) that exposed a forest of curly chest hair. Instead of naughty ungrateful teens Panjwani senior found us kids simulating a swordfight with the paint lids as our shields.

Panjwani senior glared at our jousting as if our effort were only a third class re-enactment of a medieval battle. Senior quickly then went around the car to check if any hubcaps from his beloved banana-yellow Toyota were missing. The hubcaps were, of course, all there, shiny and sneering back at him. Panjwani senior sniffed loudly, gave us another angry and bewildered look, snorted at us and walked off briskly. Lalji dropped his paint lid to create another bit of a racket. Panjwani Senior whipped his neck around, saw that resistance was futile, and went on his way leaving us to convulse in our mirth.

It turned out that that the hubcaps Panjwani senior sold in his store were imitations from China and not an original spare part from Japan. Like most things from China in those days, the hubcaps never exactly fit. And with the constant pounding of the wheels on Nairobi's bumpy roads, the hubcaps would jiggle in resonance, loosen, and eventually fall off somewhere.

Tears and Fears

The country bus heading to Limuru was speeding at 50 MPH in a 30 MPH zone. Like most country bus drivers, speed was an essential element to display power and male domination. The bus drivers would pretend to be in the East African Safari, an annual highlight of Kenyan sports and a world famous car race. Most aspiring drivers (me included) had hopes for competing in this challenging event. We imagined racing our blazing fast engines through deep volcanic mud, semi-deserts, and African savannah filled with wildebeest and zebras that couldn't understand traffic signs. The country bus drivers (and other similar fools), believed they could do one better by imagining they could win the race drunk.

As a former British colony, we drove on the left-hand side of the road. Steering wheels for all vehicles, save for any American curiosity bought by flamboyant doctors and the like, were on the right hand side.

The packed bus of tired workers hurtled downhill, past Sclaters Road and gathered momentum. The bus driver saw a car try to make a last minute turn off into a side road. It was too late for the drunken cowboy on wheels to avoid this car. So the bus driver did the next best thing. He crossed the median to oncoming traffic and crashed into a green Volkswagen bug in a massive head-on collision, flattening the empty metal of the hood where engines in most cars are found.

I know, because I was there.

For the sake of variety, Mum had decided on the spur of the moment to go to a mosque in Pangani, a few miles away from our Parklands home. Pangani mosque was mostly frequented by Ismailis who couldn't afford to live in Parklands. Mummy thought that attending mosque here would be more restful and devoid of the pomp and circumstance that normally characterized Friday services in Parklands. My Granny Fatu, little sister Rozy and the older Ferry were all in the car. In addition, in this very tiny little Beetle, packed with five of us, Mum decided to give our neighbor and her good friend Shirin a ride to the mosque. On Shirin's lap sat her little daughter Jenny.

I saw the twin headlights coming down the slope, in for the kill. The pair of lights were dull and dim-witted, but seemed fiercely dangerous like the all the idiots who drive drunk or stoned.

After a loud bang and few seconds of metal screeching upon metal, crunch and shattering glass, it was silent. I was pulled out of the car but lost my glasses, so I couldn't see well but I knew I didn't have a scratch on me. Nothing hurt. Being the skinniest, I was sandwiched between Ferry and Shirin and locked into place. I didn't even suffer from whiplash. It was as if I had never been there.

Ferry got her head snapped back and spent a few days in hospital, My Granny had deep lacerations on her face from shards of the cracked windshield; Shirin and her daughter sitting in the back seat had a few bumps and bruises. My Mummy had a steering wheel stuck in her sternum. The doctors did all they could, but Mummy died two weeks later.

The funeral was attended by a massive throng of friends and well wishers. My mother was a sensitive, delicate, soft-spoken woman without any flash, and everyone, yes everyone, liked her. She was a young woman, just over 40, and left behind three kids and a very dazed husband. I had always thought Papa would die first for he was very partial to Johnny Walker Red and had a two pack a day habit. After Mummy passed, he went on a binge, feeling sorry for himself every evening, sitting in his PJs after work and downing glass after glass of whiskey.

Ferry and I were terrified of losing another parent. We could become orphans. From our reading of Dickens and Twain we knew that orphans had a horrible or dangerous future ahead of them. So, in effect, Ferry and I (mostly Ferry) found a way to purge our grief and became Papa's caretaker. We couldn't risk another loss. Granny Fatu took over responsibility for Rozy, and after the forty days of mourning were over, the sweetest little girl on the planet (my little sister Rozy) went to Fatu's home in Mombasa, 300 miles away.

Ferry became a bonafide star and went into immediate rescue mode. She stepped into the shoes as de-facto household leader at the tender age of 16, cooking and supervising chores. She was helped by our maid, Maria, who was so bereft at my mother's loss that she began drinking "Changaa" or Kikuyu moonshine. This was all the more surprising for us, because until then Maria had been a devout Pentecostal Christian and teetotaler.

Life in the fragile little battered flat # 46 continued and our wounds still abounded and were weirdly deep. We were smothered with pity by our aunts and uncles. I didn't like being pitied since the focus of attention would be on me. All I wanted to do was crawl into a hole and cut off my head.

But it was my childhood pals, Lalji, Aloo, Khanbhai, Alnashir, Virani and Cockeyed, who lifted me out. We were sitting in middle field and Lalji was on some doozy of a fabricated story pointing out that Panjwani's mother took showers in gumboots. Panjwani reddened, and lashed out at Lalji, flinging an arm. Contact was made. Now, Panjwani was a strong squat boy like his hairy Dad, but lighter Lalji would have none of it. The bravest of us braves, Lalji didn't punch back. Instead he stood up like the leader he was, and said, "You want to fight? Let's have a fair fight. Go ahead and hit me!"

Panjwani saw the glint of determination in Lalji's soft brown eyes and backed down.

Lalji continued with his volley of pre-juvenile insults. It wasn't long before someone mentioned that someone's mother was caught wearing cowboy boots to bed. It was a lie, of course. But with the bushel of imaginative, ribald inanities we flung at each other, I finally began to laugh again.

Wrestling

During recess one day we saw trucks come up and set up a wrestling ring in the hockey stadium across from our primary school. By evening they had set up large signs announcing the exhibition of world-class wrestlers from such exotic faraway places as Romania, Jamaica, Nigeria and Scotland. The names of the wrestlers were also strikingly attractive. Honey-Boy Simba was the name of a clever competitor with flowing, pretty golden hair. Khanbhai and Nishu took an instant liking to this name and became devout and instant fans of the exquisitely proportioned Goldilocks. Other names were intriguing to us. There was the inappropriately named Frank Vulva, and a horribly strange looking guy with extra long wiry black hair who went by the name Madman Rasputin.

Cockeyed (Shiraz Virjee) and I immediately gravitated to a poster of "Prince Kumali," a tall, muscular sort with the intensity of an angry black slave. Many years later when I saw *Roots* in the United States, I knew the prototype for Kunta Kinte had to have been our beloved Prince Kumali.

Prince Kumali was dressed in leopard-print shorts and had a frighteningly large head. It was no surprise then that Prince Kumali's weapon of choice was the head butt; a sudden, excruciating and often disabling blow to an opponent's forehead. Unbeknownst to us, the white or "Mzungu" promoters in keeping with their view of Africa, had purposely advertised the only two black wrestlers among the group as having "thick skulls". So when hit by Prince Kumali's head, most foes would be concussed out of the fight. This sudden fall of a potentially ferocious competitor was proof to us that the head butt was wrestling's most important move. However, to get someone to hold his head still while smashing it like a cracked coconut with one's own forehead meant one had to first tire the opponent.

This meant the usual tricks of body slamming, sucker punches, and half-Nelsons. We grimaced when a wrestler was hurled into a post, clutching his back after impact was made. But like babies, these guys had recuperative powers that amazed us. Many would come back after incessant beatings to make a fight of it, and sometimes even came back to win. The winner of the bout was the first to make two pins or submissions. Another way to win was to knock out someone for the count of ten. Here the mighty head butt ruled.

In the flats, the boy with the thickest skull was Champee, our resident bully. Champee was a royal pain since he was strong and sadistic. We hated to play with him whether it was marbles, cricket, hockey, or football since he had no sense of fairness. He would want to win by bending rules and outright lies. When things didn't go his way, such as an indisputable goal or fallen wicket, he would search for the weakest of us and begin his torture. Typically this meant feasting on Khanbhai, Minu or me. Once he pinned my shoulders to the ground and stuffed my face with grass. He said I was a cow for getting his wicket and argued that if I was so good at getting him out I should be rewarded with a fine meal.

When Champee wasn't around, we joked that his malaise and our torture was caused by a metal plate in his head that caught malingering brain waves sent by savages, pygmies and aliens. When the wrestling season was in full swing this was all the more reason to avoid him like the plague. We all feared his strange desires to scramble the mush in our heads. Yet things miraculously went our way.

Champee was not only a pain to us, but he was also a champion violator in his own home. He regularly beat up on his three sisters and brought his mother to tears or invoked blood-curdling screams. So when some straw broke, his father sent Champee off to live with his uncle who managed a coffee farm near Nyeri, about a hundred miles away, we were elated. We could now continue to train as aspiring wrestlers without the fear of being killed.

Our wrestling practice sessions were staged in the soft, lush grass growing across from Khanbhai's house. The grass served as a cushion for some of our more inventive falls and likely prevented a few injuries. One of the more interesting moves we tried was the "Caber-Toss" a signature of Jock Cameron, the beefy Scottish professional. Cameron fought in a kilt and wrested some kind of world title away from the then title holder, Frank Vulva. The Caber-Toss required ferocious strength to literally pick up an opponent by the heels and toss him away like an unwanted pole. Among us kids, only the oak-like Cockeyed could demonstrate this ably.

While I didn't have the strength to dominate physically, I perfected a slick move that initially gave me some respect in the ring. My tactic was to trick someone to succumb to what we adults now know as the standard missionary position. With my opponents back and shoulders held to the ground, I would quickly press upon his legs, count to three and win a point. There was no escaping. At the time, we were barely 11 or 12, we had little notion of the sexual suggestiveness of the position. But noticing the inventiveness and elegance of the move, other boys followed suit and copied me.

One Saturday we decided to have a wrestling competition and it wasn't long before several bouts were concluded with a parade of boy coupling. Khanbhai's mother, watching out for her son behind lace curtains, finally couldn't stand this apparent perversion. She stormed out of her house and shouted, to Lalji and Virani who were struggling to force each other into the nefarious position, "Stop it, chokras (boys)! That's not a good thing to do!"

Khanbhai had to save face. No one liked to have his mother for interrupt our fun, and so he voiced back in exasperation, "But Mummy, what's wrong? We are only wrestling!"

"Well you shouldn't wrestle like that," replied Khanbhai's mum rather harshly.

Nishu the ever inquisitive asked, "Why?"

Khanbhai's mom puffed up in embarrassment mixed with some rage and said, "Because you are not grown up enough to do that!"

To us young pre-pubescent boys this was a shining example of a non-sequitur. Adults using wrestling moves? For what purpose? We just didn't get it.

My love of wrestling continued for a few more months and I began to train regularly. "I am the winner again, the unbeaten champion wrestler," I would exclaim as I pinned the shoulders of my regular foe onto the ground using my knees and counting off the required three seconds. Despite my sizable lack of brawn, I never cheated against this opponent. The fight had to be fair. Illegal moves such as hair pulling or biting were simply not kosher and firmly disallowed. We had to go strictly by the rule book.

I quickly reached a record of 39 -0 against my nemesis, and arch rival, for the mantle of Champion Wrestler. With my victories, I knew I deserved the prize and the accolades of whoever we imagined was watching our grand spectacle. Sometimes we had a stadium full of screaming fans while on other occasions it was a select invited few, such as the President and Pele, who got to watch our extraordinary and riveting battles.

My foe really stood no chance against my might. She was, after all, Rozy, my little sister and eight years my junior. And while I recognized her efforts as brave and exemplary, my speed, agility and strength were no match for her four year old body.

There was barely anyone else in the flats against who I could win any wrestling match. So to lay claim to any kind of title I had fight my hapless little sister, over and over again. Rozy was an excellent sport about this. She never ratted on her losses or went whining to Mummy after a hyperextension of whatever sort. This was sportsmanship, I told her. A true hero never whines.

But, when Mummy caught me twisting my opponent's arm around the back in an obviously awkward and painful position, my wrestling career came to an abrupt halt. Mummy sat me down and explained that Rozy wasn't a toy; she was my little sister, and that as a far bigger boy I could cause some serious problems for her down the road. I immediately called off all fights after being threatened by Mummy that my behavior could be referred to our home's supreme disciplinary commander (i.e. Papa).

There was no worse torture than a long lecture by my father. Chinese water torture didn't even come close, and neither did waterboarding in any of the forms the CIA was perfecting. So, I immediately held a small press conference, the empty couch and pictureless TV listening intently, and shed away my goodbye tears. But I knew I was retiring from wrestling as a decorated champion. Yes, I was a worthy and unbeaten champion of flat # 46, and I'll take that title to my grave.

Mr. Mccormick

Passage into high school is a momentous occasion for most. It most certainly was for me as well. Apart from Mummy's death, I can't think of a single thing that had a bigger impact.

In Kenya, after seven years of primary school, one took a national examination, the Certificate of Primary Education (CPE) to determine which high school was available to you. If one was rich, you could apply to a handful of expensive private or parochial schools run by nuns or their equivalent.

We weren't rich, so we had to achieve great results to get into some of the premier high schools. At the time, there were three state funded "pearls" in the City; Jamhuri High (formerly the Duke of Gloucester), Lenana School (Duke of York), and Nairobi School (The Prince of Wales). Staffed by excellent teachers sent by the British taxpayers as "development aid" or as guilty repayment for years of colonial plunder, these schools were highly selective. One had to pass the CPE with almost flying colors to get accepted. Jamhuri High, a day school, was filled with smart Hindus sporting gobs of Brylcream or hair oil to radiate an ultra black sheen or to simply keep it in place. I never knew which. I hated hair oil which was one reason I wasn't attracted to enter this domain of bright Indian-Kenyans (Patels, Shahs, Kumars and a smattering of Sunnis, Lohanas, and Sikhs) and a large pool of very capable black Kenyans.

As a meat eater, I also thought the eating habits of the Hindus were strange. Sure they looked like many of us Ismailis, and we spoke and understood the same languages at home (Hindi, Punjabi and Gujarati), but the lack of meat in their diets apparently made them smell funny and over spiced. I had nothing against spice; Mummy used tons of it her Indian dishes.

But the Hindus seemingly over use of the asphyxiating "Hing" or "Devils Dung", a staple spice in Indian vegetarian cooking, was a ghastly way to add flavor. (Reader: If you haven't put your nose in a bottle of Hing, I urge you to first take out a life insurance policy. The smell could kill you). So Jamhuri High was out.

I could have also attended the Aga Khan High School, but sister Ferry was already there, and she insisted that I not join her school. She was convinced I would embarrass her with my idiocy and limit her access to cute boys. Well, that was fine. I never wanted to be around her pompous big-girl airs anyway.

As luck would have it, enter Mr. McCormick, an imposing looking but genial Scotsman. McCormick was a housemaster at Nairobi School and dispatched to recruit prize students at our primary school. Miss Kassam, our principal and a thin reed of woman with a squeaky voice, ordered all high school-bound boys to gather in the assembly hall. I was excited. This was a big deal, almost a rite of passage, and none of those idiotic girls who so easily embarrassed me would be present.

McCormick talked of "Houses" where students could board, of school spirit and intramural sports, of vast, impeccable grounds, and the strict discipline that would turn little momma's boys into men. I was thoroughly impressed by McCormick. Desirous of big muscles and the promise of manhood, I had to apply.

Soon after the CPE results came out, I received a letter from Nairobi School noting that I had been accepted. Mummy, Ferry and I were ecstatic for different but obvious reasons. Young Rozy looked on smiling, excited to be part of some type of celebration. I think all of us viewed our family's closeness and happiness through the barometer of Rozy's twinkling eyes. Rozy was such a magical little girl that when Mummy died about two years later, I thought her smile lost some of its vivacity, her eyes dulled and none of us would ever fully recover.

Papa seemed happy that I got into a fine educational institution and he showed this with a grunt of assent. But he then also lectured me on how I should have done as well as Aleem on the CPE exams. He pointed out that I now had to prove myself in a much bigger arena, and so shouldn't waste time reading storybooks. I would need to crack open big fat text books, he said, like those Ferry already used, and it made no sense filling my head with fantasy.

Fearing reprisals from Papa, I stopped reading for about a week and focused on maths and history. The short interlude was all I could muster, and pretty soon I got back to reading. Reading Enid Blyton books were my secret passion then. I scoured Chandani's, our neighborhood second-hand bookstore for any of her masterpieces on *The Famous Five, Five Found-Outers and Dog, The Secret Seven* or *Mallory Towers*.

Early in high school, I moved on to reading the "Biggles" series of books by Capt. W.E. John. Biggles was a crack RAF pilot who had brought down scores of German Messerschmitts with his modest single engine Spitfire. Since I now was at Nairobi School, a bastion and remaining vestige of colonial Britain, it only seemed appropriate to focus on World War II heroes. I convinced myself that because I was attending Nairobi School I simply couldn't let down Queen and Country. So I ignored Papa's further calls to stop my pleasure reading.

The emphatic approval and license to enjoy a lifetime of reading was given to me by Mr. Weeks, our English teacher in Form 2. On the first day of class, this red-bearded prophet, with a pleasant, open smile and round glasses like Lennon's, announced: "Whatever, you need to learn about English, you can't study by staring blankly at grammar books. The only way to master English is by reading."

"Read anything, but especially read novels," Mr. Weeks urged. "When you read extensively, you will learn how to write. You will not need to memorize rules for avoiding split-infinitives or understanding compound adjectives. In this class you will only read and write. English will come naturally to you."

Mr. Weeks' words sent me soaring. Boy, did I feel like James Bond! I now had a non-expiring, lifetime license to read! That evening, I rushed to tell Mummy and Papa of this wonderful pronouncement made by our new teacher. I emphasized to Papa, when he begin to argue, that Mr. Weeks was a super smart, real-live Englishman who was teaching English at none other than the school formerly known as Prince of Wales. I said there was nothing Papa could do to usurp this authority, unless the Queen or Prince came home for tea and admonished me in person. Papa mumbled something and grunted but Mummy had a big smile on her face for she was a reader too.

I read incessantly after that; mostly adventure and mystery novels, and I learned to make up stories. In fact, to you, dear reader, I ask if you think what I have written so far is mostly fantasy?

A Sporting Life

Before my first day at the former Prince of Wales High School, now boringly named Nairobi School, we were mailed orientation instructions. We were told where to report, the correct way to wear our uniforms and polish our shoes, and to keep our stockings up at all times by using tight elastic garters that impeded blood flow to the calves. The instructions also noted to which of the six "houses" we would forever be duty and honor bound. These houses were named after famous British folk who had done some kind of great service to the Queen or King of England. My own house, Clive, was named after Baron Robert Clive the rampaging General who played a large hand in keeping India under British Control in the 18th Century. The other houses were Scott, Grigg, Hawke, Nicholson, and Rhodes.

This notion of "houses" demanded strict loyalty and subservience to the older boys in the house. I assumed that this type of discipline was in keeping with British military tradition and necessary in case Kenya got attacked by the nefarious Somalis from up North. I observed that the discipline we obtained would prepare us for soldiering, and we would put up the good fight against those pesky "miraa" chewing bandit-nomads.

Even before we got our books, all entering first formers were herded in groups to the store room. There we were asked to which "house" we belonged. Each of us replied dutifully and were then given two sports jerseys in "house" colors. Clive House was signified by a pristine white, Scott boys got a dark purple, Hawke a light blue and so on.

The very first year of school was a reprieve of some kind. Most of us first formers were nothing more than small boys and many still with baby fat and scant pubic hair. To help get acclimatized to the school's far and wide ranging set of rules, and to develop a loyalty for our eventual senior house we were first nursed at a junior house. We still had to maintain loyalty to our senior house, but we weren't' required to represent it in intra-mural sports. Moreover there weren't any senior boys harassing us into becoming sport machines. But that all changed when we hit the second form.

On the first day of making it to the "senior houses" we newly-minted second formers were assembled like cows heading to the abattoir. In explicit terms we were instructed to wear our house jerseys whenever we represented the house for any sporting activity. Failure to do so meant an instant hour of "Working Party," a form of chain gang, where one was forced to cut grass, sweep floors or clean toilets. I had plenty of incentive not to screw up, since I had never cleaned a toilet or mowed a lawn. (At home we were spoiled little Indian boys, pampered by ser-vants, mothers and sisters).

We found out the range of sporting events at the senior houses was wide and rotated by semester. Rugby, soccer and field hockey were the compulsory sports for our three term academic year, but cricket, cross-country, swimming, tennis, and marksmanship were optional. (Yes, we even had a rifle range to practice just in case the Somalis were stupid enough to attack). At the end of the first week of this move to the senior house, all boys were told to assemble for a "weigh-in". Rugby teams for intra-mural activity we were informed would be based on weight. This made sense since weight was a proxy for strength and size. Since rugby is a menacing, ligament-shredding, and bone-breaking sport normally played by big oafs, I hoped I would be placed in the "lightest" category or Junior Colts. As one of the skinniest boys in school I didn't want to get killed on the pitch. As luck would have it I *was* placed in Junior Colts and I thanked God profusely that day for not being a bigger boy.

Our first match was against arch rival Scott House. Scott House was down the cloister from us, and facing the school's immaculate quadrangle. Scott and my house, Clive, had the best physical setting in school; neither could claim an edge there.

The whistle blew and the match began. My coke-bottle spectacles were off my face (one didn't play rugby with glasses on) and I couldn't see a thing. Slimily, I claimed the left wing or tail end of the formation, the place reserved for the fastest on the team. It was where I thought one would be least likely to be hammered. The ball headed toward our side of the pitch. We were now to advance the ball to our opponent's goal posts for a try. This mean a quick succession of passing, until the fastest guy (apparently, yours truly) got the ball whereupon he would run like the wind for three points.

The ball eventually came my way after a set of precision passes by my team upfront. But from the haze formed by my lack of vision, all I saw was an opposing thundering herd of angry wildebeest ready to crush me into mango pulp. This was no game! This was slaughter. I threw the back the ball to a teammate as if it were a hot potato, in effect stalling our drive. The place exploded with laughter. Everyone saw how terrified I was, and so my rugby career had come to a quick end. It was not that I was no use to the team. It was far worse than that. My silliness actually allowed the opposing team –Scott House - to score first. Faced with the specter of such a woeful teammate, the coach (a senior boy at Clive) excused me. I never played rugby again and still have all my front teeth to attest for that.

Field hockey was only slightly better. Although I played some in our flats, hockey at school was a far more serious affair. With the bulk of the teams made of beefy, muscular Africans wielding hockey sticks like machetes, I felt like I was in the thick of a riot without a cause to support. There was constant jostling, tripping and shin-smacking to get to the ball. So I perfected a way to avoid contact at any cost, milling around the periphery of action like Neptune or Pluto orbiting the Sun. This scintillating display of sportsmanship again led me to be excused from the game. So while I was now part of a stable considered the school weaklings, I didn't have any broken bones.

But house rules meant if you didn't play on any of the house teams, you had to support them for key matches. Rollcall was taken for those not on the pitch, and an unexcused absence immediately led to a sessions of "working party". Noting that I would never be any use on the field, a sixth former and prefect insisted that I serve as resident cheerleader. I was to attend every rugby game played by Clive House's senior team, and I was to scream on support for my mates on the pitch. If I was in America, I would probably have been forced to put on a skirt, shake pom-poms and do the Texas two-step. I look back and thank the stars that the odd sort of cheering that occurs in America, of miniskirts, jiggling boobs and swaying hips, hadn't yet been imported to Kenya.

The constant cheering was a bore but at least I traded certain death for tedious screeching. However one morning at the 8 AM daily roll call, I was informed that I was to represent the house in an intra-mural cross country meet. What? This most certainly was some kind of mistake for everyone knew I was the slowest guy in the house. Furthermore this was Kenya, which raised the best runners in the world. Our high school had won the national cross country championship for two years running, and I wasn't going to compete against some slouches. These were bona fide potential Olympic medalists. How would I match up with the school's fastest runners who imitated gazelles running away from hungry lions?

My meek protests to drop me from the race fell on deaf ears. I was to run or face suspension, an ignominy far worse than working party. So I ran. I began the eight mile trek around the vast school compound at a furious pace. Geez, I was keeping up with the fastest, and I was feeling great. Endorphins were quickly flooding my brain. But by the time we passed the 200 yard mark, I knew that running wasn't something I could conquer. The pack got ahead of me and there was no way I could run a mile. And doing eight miles across hilly terrain was a downright silly proposition.

Feigning a hamstring pull I stopped, clutched my stick-like thigh with conviction and slunk back for home. The omnipresent prefect with the clipboard checked off my name and so I received full-marks for trying. But the obvious hilarity of my effort, also granted me a full reprieve to avoid any further sporting activity for the house. This was the best news since I arrived at school, since I also inferred that didn't have to stand and cheer those rugby playing dolts banging their heads and scrambling their brains. I wasn't the king of any sport, but I *was* a cunning little weasel and I desperately needed this trait to survive in the land of giants and strict discipline.

It was my table tennis skills honed in my primary school years that initially saved me from the fate at being labeled as a useless, good for nothing skinny, Mummy's boy. In the junior house we had an adequate ping-pong table, and since we played "winner stays," I often held the table for many games in succession. This irked one of the bigger boys, KH, to no end. KH hated to see me win. One day as I was giving someone else a sound thrashing, KH slipped *his* two hands into *my* khaki shorts, and pulled them down. He could do this with ease since I had an elastic waistband to hold my shorts rather than buttons and a belt. Getting caught with my pants down was bad enough, but the worst part was that I didn't wear underwear and my privates came on full display – the full Monty, as it were. With my boy-manhood exposed, the crowd, which I believed had assembled to see my fine ping pong talent, burst into laughter and jeered. Apparently I was the only boy in school who didn't wear underwear. This meant I was a clueless moron and had much to learn.

Having my pants pulled down was a nasty bit of work by KH, but it underscored that life would be cruel in high school if I didn't completely blend in. Inevitably, when I reached home that day (I was a day boy and not a boarder) I asked Mummy to drive immediately to Haria Cash Stores in the City Centre. There I knew I could get khaki shorts with buttons and white underwear with a "Y front." I had to show everyone else I could tough it out. The unwarranted display of my bum was only the first of many such embarrassing incidents that forced me to leave the safety of sheltered boyhood.

Discipline

Our first year housemaster was the ultra-strict disciplinarian, Mr. Pullan. Pullan also taught metalwork, and had responsibility for the school shop that contained all kind of lathes, saws, grinding machines and whatever else craftsmen use to turn blocks of dull metal into usable stuff. Spending decades banging, hammering and lifting heavy metals, Mr. Pullan developed the arms of Hercules. He was a frightening sight with his fiery red hair, a deep menacing voice, and a body that could have rivaled Schwarzenegger's. In reality Pullan was probably a pussy-cat, but he used his demeanor to bring order to a group of 50 crybabies.

Most of us day boys came from Nairobi's wealthy or middle class Asian families, who could afford to drop off their beloved boys to school by car. When the day ended, and other boarders had chores and assignments to do, we "day bugs" were driven home safely to the confines of Mummy.

Pullan was well aware of this. He knew it was up to him to begin the long process of turning a bunch of screeching, spoiled wimps into men and he took his job seriously. On our first day he assembled us inside the common room of our junior house. As we sat with rapt attention mesmerized by his bulging, twitching muscles he said in explicit terms that we were a bunch of weenies, and that our Nairobi School experience would be far removed from our pampered lives of home.

Pullan then called each of us to meet him so he could put the name to a face. When we stood before him, he looked at us squarely in the eye, as if searching for hair lice or unwanted boogers. He then let each of us sit down without saying a word to us. When he had finished his visual inspection, he announced, "You are all deplorable and undisciplined. High school is not a holiday. You will be clean and have sparkling uniforms. You will behave like gentlemen and listen to your teachers and the senior boys. Every Friday morning I will inspect each of you in the quadrangle before the school wide assembly."

I felt my bowels loosening. What had I gotten myself into? I was to be immaculate and answer to everyone senior to me? It was pain enough for me to look passably tidy each day, but then to also answer to senior boys who I knew would be mean bullies? I thought I had joined a gulag and not high school. Over the months I found my fears were not unfounded. To the senior boys in forms five and six, we first and second formers were simply known as "fags". As fags, school tradition meant that we had to serve as bonded slaves, performing inane chores such as making tea and polishing shoes, and to run around the quad for no apparent reason except to sweat. If we didn't obey, these older boys had the authority to send us to working party on Saturday afternoons where we would be subject to even higher forms of torture.

Pullan's Friday morning inspections were terrifying. Our uniforms had to be perfect and smartly pressed; stockings would be held up by elastic garters, our black-laced shoes polished well enough to reflect the anxiety in our faces, and our fingernails clipped. Long hair was not permitted, and any attempt to develop locks was sanctioned. Even an imprecise tie knot could result in a violation. Any boy failing inspection would be summoned to an individual meeting with Pullan where appropriate punishment such as detention, working party or six of the best would be meted out. We had had heard that instead of a bamboo cane, Pullan whipped boys with a metal rod. This rumor was enough to change our demeanor toward discipline in a week.

As far as we knew only the school principal, the Second Master (vice-principal) or one's Housemaster was allowed to mete out corporal punishment. I don't know who made that rule, but that's what it was. We were naturally terrified of housemaster Pullan, but to my knowledge the only persons he possibly caned in "Junior Day House" during my first year were Rana and Keshavjee.

This pair of idiots would entertain us after lunch by staging mock fights replete with flying karate kicks, precise uppercuts and the accompanying deep grunts of fake pain and effort. One particular fight was a restaging of the fight James Bond had with his nemesis in a tiny railway compartment in *From Russia with Love*. Some of us had seen the movie, and we egged on the boys to demonstrate how 007 could get the upper hand in tight quarters. Things quickly got out of control, and Rana flung a chair at Keshavjee out of frustration. The chair missed its mark and crashed through the large plate glass window in our common room. Since there were plenty of witnesses, the dumb perpetrators were forced into Pullan's office to receive what they deserved. When they re-emerged, both had wide grins on their faces. These two crazies had relished that they had survived Pullan's wrath. They never said if they were caned, but they were suspended for two weeks and so the myth of Pullan's metal rod remained unproven.

Prefects at Nairobi School meted out discipline like dung from elephants on laxatives. Puffed up by self- importance, they behaved like Hitler Youth terrorizing us young ones with obsessively mean interpretations of school or house violations. One could spot prefects from a distance since they were required to wear cravats instead of ties. We would signal each other when in the vicinity of a prefect and this method for avoiding punishment usually worked, but not always. Inevitably, some of us would plunge down the ravine of a clearly visibly violation resulting in punishment called "working party". For example, if one's tie was not fully knotted, or if one showed off a calf when a stocking untidily reached an ankle, you were subject to working party. Major offences, including cigarette smoking or fighting, would mean working party and reporting to the housemaster, where more punishment awaited.

Working party was a poor euphemism of what really occurred. It wasn't a party of the least kind, tea, dance, political, or otherwise. It was simply an hour and a half of interminable drudgery. Having committed a grievous error, the prefects believed that those on the "party" should be punished with horribly disgusting tasks such as cleaning shit-shards stuck fast to the white of the porcelain bowls. Another task was to polish a pair of muddy shoes until we could see our reflections in the leather. The easiest task was to pull out weeds or cut and shape lawns until they looked good enough to play a cup final at Wembley Stadium. The very silly notion of "party" came in because no one could get dismissed until the idiot-maroons, as Bugs might say, inspected all the work done and gave it collective approval. Upon very close inspection by these cruel prefects, our work was often found wanting. This led to them arbitrarily adding more time or more chores for our lack of discipline. The prefects made it explicitly known that fortitude was developed by adhering strictly to our chores. But even the prefects could not always win. Overbearing punishments could be brought to the housemaster and the prefect could be overruled. This was a major embarrassment to those who thought they had the qualities to lead future armies of corporate or political warriors. So there was a semblance of just and unjust, tilted of course in our view, to the unjust.

But rules are meant to be broken, especially by kids who want to show off how much they can get away with. Save for the athletic fields, walking on any kind of school lawn was not permitted. Walking on the pristine main quadrangle was to commit hara-kiri. The knolls of grass we risked walking on were far away from the center of school. One fine day, I was late for biology class. I thought I could save precious few seconds and potential teacher admonishment by cutting across a few yards of lawn. As luck or discipline would have it, I ran into Awimbo, our Head Prefect. He stopped me, first inspecting me for any clothing violations. Barely satisfied with what he saw, he asked me to write a thousand lines stating, "I will not walk on the grass especially near the biology labs." If anyone reading this hasn't tried to write a thousand lines in pencil, please do not try. I can vouch that it simply is hell.

Biology class also served as an important footnote and reminder of another failing. The labs were ringed with large hibiscus bushes that bloomed prodigiously and lent a nice red-orange contrast to our sea of blue uniforms. In one of my first biology lectures, Mr. Nganga gave each of us a hibiscus flower to dissect. We were specifically told we had to show careful skill and to uncover the stamens and pistil for prominent display. We were also told that our grade for this exercise would depend on the skill with which we conducted the dissection, and that we would each only get one flower. Since I thought I could be Dr. Kildare (Richard Chamberlain) with his superb good looks and a pleasant bedside manner, I rushed to finish the dissection. As luck would have it, I botched the job, rendering the pretty flower into an unrecognizable mess. This was not good, and I didn't want to fail the test. So I snuck out of the lab to snatch another specimen perched on a bush just a few yards away.

When I returned, Mr. Nganga, stood there with his arms folded while my face reddened. "You are a flower thief," he barked, the anger in his face causing beads of perspiration to stream down his face. He quickly scribbled a note and instructed me to go to Mr. Packwood and to return it to him signed.

My legs turned into rubber and I barely made the trip to Packwood's office without collapsing. Stealing, I knew, was a crime worse that throwing a chair through a plate glass window. If Rana and Keshavjee were suspended from school for their crime, I knew my punishment would be far more severe. Expulsion was a certainty. I dreaded what Papa would say, and Mummy would be so disappointed with her beloved boy. The humiliation I would bring to my family was unfathomable. Ferry would have a field day telling all her friends about my criminal bent, and I'd simultaneously become the biggest pariah and laughing stock in all of East Africa.

Packwood was a chain smoking, fat fart with stringy white hair and a double chin. Like most teachers, he was probably harmless but then what did I know? He looked at the note, repressed a grin but I saw the twinkle in his eye. Dang! Not only was I going to be kicked out but he was going to be cruel and have fun doing this. Packwood told me to bend over, and in quick succession he caned me twice with a yellow bamboo cane.

"You have been punished," said Packwood in a nonchalant tone as he signed the note to take back to Nganga. "Don't steal flowers again."

Was that it? No expulsion? I went outside and looked up at the sky through my thick glasses. I squinted at the brilliant Nairobi sunshine and thanked the lord and his flies for once again saving the little fool that was me. The red stripes on my thighs were a badge of honor to display to my mates, and I strode confidently back into class with the air of a freed slave.

Cricket

A saving grace that allowed me to be accepted by the other boys was my love for cricket. When I arrived at Nairobi School we had a really good first XI. The suave, swashbuckling Virjee brothers, Naguib and Nasoor with their array of in-swingers, fast pace bowling, and flashy bats made us the school to beat. On Sundays at the tender age of 16 and 18, the brothers played Club cricket, the apex of Kenyan cricket. Another outstanding pair, the Malik brothers, was also on the school's first team. Combined, this set of four with additional strength from other determined Indians, made us school unbeatable. Our nemesis, St. Mary's, full of white boys and wealthy Asians, suffered in silence as we beat them four straight years.

My dream was to play for the school First XI. But to do that, I knew it had to be a journey of sheer perseverance. I thought I was quite good, having honed my skills at home in the sloping middle field but I knew I had to start at the bottom. Our school fielded four teams, the First XI, Second XI, Senior Colts, and Junior Colts composed mostly of first and second formers. I tried out for the Junior Colts – most Indian first former boys did.

In my first year, I was still a skinny runt with poor speed. With my growth hormones still dormant I didn't have power or height. It's not that I would ever develop power, but height allowed for faster deliveries. With my tiny frame and lack of strength, I was accurately viewed by most of having distinct disadvantages.

The Junior Colts were coached by Reverend Davies, the school chaplain and organist. The Rev. was an uppity WASP harboring the old fashioned notion that good fielding, front foot always forward, and a straight bat were keys to success. He even wore his collar to practice, imploring the Lord to be on our side. I didn't think God was an able cricketer, but then I was terrified of the Almighty at that age, and confused about religion. I knew the deck was already stacked against me.

At our try-out the Reverend was not impressed with my spindly physique, and he put me out to pasture at deep square leg. It was unlikely I would see any action, since hitting to square leg required skill and power that few boys could manage at that age. I wanted to bowl, but the lankier and stronger boys were immediately chosen to display their hurling skills. So for most of the try-out session I stood there like a stiff at square leg with nothing to do except scratch my ass.

I did get a chance to display my defensive batting prowess, but I knew that my anemic batting skills alone wouldn't compel the Rev. to select me. I thought I excelled at bowling but without a chance to show off my pace and accuracy, I saw my cricket career coming to a quick end. If I didn't make the Junior Colts, it was unlikely I would get the experience to move on to the senior teams.

By my counting, spots quickly filled up by kids who could bowl well, showed promise at batting or merely looked good in the slips. Bending their knees low so as to give the air of professionalism, the guys at first and second slip and gulley even looked the part.

I knew that the Reverend had made up his mind on at least eight or nine of the boys when a fellow who we nicknamed Rhino, on account for his very large nose, thought he would display his power. He came to the crease, and with a couple of swings, he showed he belonged. Dang! I had little hope now. But then with his next swing, Rhino turned to show off how good he was and he hit the ball directly to square leg. The well struck red missile came directly to me to with speed and ferocity. I had no time to think, and all I could do was apply instinct. I closed my eyes and stuck out my hand. As if by magic the ball stuck to my palm. It was a brilliant one handed catch! The Reverend clapped and I made the team. Indeed, God was looking over me.

Two of the most notable moments of my life involved cricket. The first one was delivered to me by Papa who came to pick me up after practice one Thursday evening. It was dusk in Nairobi, a chill settling in as it often did at high altitude when the sun went down. We had had a good practice and were looking forward to our match on Saturday. I saw the family car and knew that Papa had come to watch and give judgment. I was thrilled. I was especially excited because I had captured a couple of wickets in practice, ripping the bails of the wicket in both cases. I so hoped that Papa would compliment that work of precision and would be proud of his little boy. But Pops never saw those feats, he hadn't arrived in time. Instead as we drove home he said, "You looked so small out there fielding; like a little, skinny stick." Was that all? I was so hurt buy this outrage that I didn't say a word on the way home.

Another memorable cricket event was teammate Suleman's errant throw. We had just broken for tea in a match against Technical High School, and Suleman, ever excited to bat, tossed the ball high up in the air to what he thought was a waiting Grewal. Instead, the red ball homed in on the bald, brown pate of the umpire, a teacher, chaperone, and representing Technical High. Suleman shouted, "Grewal," but the force of gravity and the velocity with which he threw the ball was too quick for anyone to make adjustments. The ball landed on the bald teacher's head, making a loud conk, and flooring the poor fellow. He was out cold for a couple of minutes and we thought he had died. Reverend Davies, in his ever-present collar, rushed to help and, I thought, to give last rites.

All of us players gathered around and then we saw the bald umpire's leg twitch. The guy was alive and pretty soon he began mumbling some nonsense. He had only suffered a concussion and we were relieved that our teammate had not committed manslaughter. Perhaps the Reverend had asked God for special dispensation that day, and saved the conked out teacher from certain death. My very slender faith in God had been slightly renewed.

Apart from claiming a wicket or making a catch, what I liked most about cricket were the cucumber sandwiches offered at tea. With crusts cut off, these little creations with just the right amount of mayonnaise could do little damage to my baby teeth. They were my favorite, although "cook" also made scrumptious scones to have with butter and jam. We were provided this luxury only because there were teachers present and had to demonstrate to the riff-raff teams from schools in Eastleigh or Pangani, how civilized and proper we were at Nairobi School.

Since we competed on a time clock, each team batting for a limited period, our matches led to an inordinate number of gentlemanly draws rather than outright victories. Even though one team might be far stronger than the other, this suited the chivalry and friendliness of the game that the teachers were trying to instill in us. The team that batted first had to declare innings at after two hours of batting. Tea was then served precisely at 4 PM, when the side that batted first finished batting. At 4:30, the other team took to bat, and had to score more runs than the other team without losing all wickets. Failure to score more runs posted by the team that went first but *not* losing all ten wickets resulted in a draw.

If we won the toss, we would usually let the other team bat first. They would score in the neighborhood of 50 to 75 runs and then it would be our turn to bat. It was especially tough for us to score more than 40 runs because I was sent as opening batsman. The teachers and everyone else for that matter believed that a new ball had considerable shine on it and that it was important to protect wickets. A new ball moves far more in the air and on the ground, which makes gauging the spin and direction tricky. However, since I had perfected the ultra defensive "front-foot forward", it was hard to get me out. It was also somewhat of a waste of an afternoon, because I rarely scored. My mundane blocking of excellent deliveries didn't do much for our run total. This was a source of frustration for the other team who clearly had scored more runs and usually had more dangerous bowlers. Yet, my boring but stellar defensive play usually ensured that our opponents could never retire our full side and most of our matches ended in a draw. We took solace in this, because we knew the other side was always better. It was far better to get a draw than it was to lose. When I finally witnessed American Football many years later, I was introduced to the notion that a tie was like "kissing one's sister." I could do without that.

In cricket, a boundary or a whack of four runs is a glorious thing. It requires skill and power to guide a ball through alert fielders and have it reach the perimeter of the pitch. Should a ball cross this line without hitting the ground when struck, six runs are awarded. Hitting a "sixer" was clearly out of my range. I was way too skinny to launch a ball sky high that would also cover 60 or so yards over the ground. Even when I made the First XI, I never hit a six in a regulation sized field. But surely I had the capability to drive a ball past "mid-off" to the boundary? I could also hit a four the easy way, using the speed of a fast bowler's delivery to slip it between "point" and "gulley". Or, if wanted a spectacular boundary and the accolades of my mates, I could risk exposing my wicket, turn around and smash it toward square leg.

This last type of strike is always difficult to do requiring a good measure of guts, strength and precision, all qualities I didn't have in abundance. To attain my goal, it had to be a forward drive or an accurate knick toward point and gulley. In most matches after about forty minutes of supremely dull defensive play, and having scored a grand total of three runs or so, I would "open" up and try to smack it to the boundary. To my chagrin I never accomplished this. Not once, nada, never.

I came close once, striking the ball with the ferocity of Conan the Barbarian but was thwarted by the excellent fielding of an opponent at point. It is an embarrassment to anyone who calls himself a cricketer to never have hit a four, and I must say I am embarrassed.

Cricket, however, was not about winning at any cost. It was about crisp white uniforms, our lovely green Oval, delicious snacks at tea, and exhibiting strange but proper manners. I'd take a polite draw any day than get pummeled. As age creeps up, my probability of accomplishing the feat of hitting a boundary diminishes. But to keep my dream alive, this will mean creaking through the next few decades trying to get past "silly-mid-off" on a senior circuit. Cricket anyone?

HP- Sauce

Some folks think I am naturally born clumsy. I'd kill for that gene if that were true. When it comes to tasks involving spatial orientation, physical strength, or fixing things, I politely inform people that I'm a walking disaster; my defect caused by eating too many bananas.

When asked, "Bananas," I reach into the bowels of nonsense to note that excessive doses of potassium present in the fruit can result in a genetic mutation. "This flaw arrests any kind of talent in manual dexterity". I tell my friends that this is why I could never be a full-fledged sports star or die-maker for precision parts. I cite the New England Journal of Medicine's (NEJM) 1973 summer issue as my source.

It's a good story, but total bullshit. The NEJM doesn't publish a summer issue, such as a greedy comic book publisher might. But my well-crafted lie leaves people impressed at my knowledge of base pairs, chromosomes and ribonucleic acid.

In high school, like all imbecile boys, we cultivated the art of feeding unsuspecting folk with imaginary tales. I learned my skills from the school champion of tall tales – my classmate Rajabali. By the age of 14, Rajabali informed us, that he had had sex with three women; not two or 20, but always a steadfast three.

He repeated incessantly, and in glorious Technicolor, the exact circumstances of each of his victories; of first scoring with a wayward girl in the dark behind the cricket pavilion, then of stealing one his father's' condoms and seducing his second cousin, and finally making it with a middle-aged German tourist at one of Mombasa's finest beach hotels.

We called his lies, "sauce," after HP Sauce, a tangy condiment that embellished any bland dish. HP sauce was a blend of sorts between Worcestershire sauce and ketchup. The bottle had on it a label with a prominent picture of the British Houses of Parliament. From this I inferred that British folk obviously loved ketchup, but since they would be loath to admit any kind of American penchant, they had to make up their own weak substitute. It was Damji who first applied the moniker of "sauce" to Rajabali's wild claims. He learned from Rajabali that HP sauce had certain berries with aphrodisiac properties not elsewhere found save in the Ngorongoro crater. Damji promptly marked this as utter nonsense and, as defacto leader of our motley crew, sent me to the library confirm this hoax. Yet we all knew there was a grain of truth in Rajabali's vast barn of stories.

Rajabali's father drove a Mercedes, which meant he was rich. Damji asked him how his father had made it big. Rajabali smiled and said, "You won't believe this, but it's true."

We were all ears for another ridiculous story. Rajabali first promised us to secrecy, and then went on to recount how his father was a diamond smuggler. That he would cross the border into Tanzania, and head to the diamond mines near Shinyanga. Once there he would pick up uncut diamonds from some local tribesmen and bring them back to Kenya hidden in the oil tank of his car. He would then fly off to Belgium and sell them for a huge profit to guys in funny, large black hats and long beards.

We thought Rajabali was off his rocker. "Diamond smuggling? Selling to an army of bearded diamond-cutters? We went into a fitful of laughter and Rajabali almost looked happy that we didn't believe him. Then one day, I noticed a short article in the *Daily Nation* that described the border arrest of an Indian rally car driver of minor fame. The charges filed against him were diamond smuggling. I brought the paper to school the next day and showed it to our posse. Could Rajabali's dad also be a smuggler?

Rajabali freaked. He reminded us that we were sworn to secrecy on what he had divulged about his father. The first thing we did, of course, was to leak this story to our parents. The arrested man's behavior was viewed as scandalous, and now our gossipy parents could share another juicy story among their friends. Within a week, Rajabali had left school; his father bundling his family and making a dash for Canada. I never saw Rajabali again.

One of the biggest, but most appealing lies Rajabali perpetrated, was that peeing into a kettle and boiling this with tea leaves made for a delicious beverage. As luck would have it I could have gotten expelled from school for even knowing about this. As second formers, and the youngest of boys in the senior house, we were duty-bound to House prefects and forced to make their afternoon tea. This "Tea trade" duty rotated amongst us second formers; the week-long penance for each of us occurred like sore lesions twice a term.

The actual "trade" involved going to the dining hall a few hundred yards away and bringing down a tray with tea leaves, fresh milk, bread, sugar and jam (no butter, however) and then preparing the repast. Merali, the boy also assigned to my trade slot for the week, objected vehemently to this role of indentured servant. So on a cold rainy afternoon, when every prefect sought a cup of tea, Merali protested by emptying his bladder into the kettle and mixed in some water. After the kettle boiled, we served it to the four waiting prefects with freshly made toast and jam.

I was aghast. I knew that tea tampering would be viewed as a very serious violation, almost as bad as dumping the stuff in a New England harbor, and that we risked expulsion. But I couldn't snitch on Merali. He had warned me that he would take me down with him if I did. Merali would insist it was my idea and that would be the end of Nairobi School for me.

We watched anxiously as the first sips were taken. One of the especially boorish prefects, Chege, looked up at us after he swallowed a big gulp. He smiled, looking oddly evil as big yellow teeth covered his very black face. We were now convinced that Merali's prank had been discovered and expulsion loomed. Instead, Chege said, "This is the finest tea I have ever had. This is really good."

Merali, the crime's perpetrator, said coolly, "Cook ran out of the regular 'Green Label' tea so he gave us 'Gold Label' instead." Gold label, a finer blend of tea leaves was normally only served in the teacher's staff room. Thinking they had got a bonus, all of the prefects downed their mugs and wolfed down their toast.

After we cleaned up, Chege came up to us and said, "We really like it when you boys do our trades. The tea is excellent and the toast is perfect." We thanked Chege for his compliment and scooted out of the door. It was another frightfully close escape in the annals of childhood.

Fun with Teachers

I did a lot of stuff to play the class fool. Like most boys I was desperate to be popular, so showing my mettle through humor and tom-foolery was a certain way to get noticed. I didn't have anything else going for me – I wasn't an excellent footballer, artist, metalworker, or even someone who could spin a good yarn. So I did the next best thing. I became really good at shooting one-lined barbs in class.

One morning our chemistry teacher Mr. Stewart held up a bottle of hydrogen peroxide and asked us if we knew what the term B.P. meant on the label. An affable Scot, who had an uncanny resemblance to the singer John Denver, Mr. Stewart said that anyone with the right answer would be awarded a free pass to miss our next test. The question even stumped Rodriguez, the boy in our class who knew most everything. (Rodriguez had nothing to do at home except to get chubby and pore over books). Sensing an immediate adoration by a bunch of classmates, I put up my hand.

Stewart asked, "And what do *you* think B.P. means, Nanji?"

I answered deadpan, "British Petroleum, sir". Mr. Stewart burst into a deep, throaty laugh and I knew I had scored some kind of victory.

"Your imagination is striking Nanji, but you are, as usual, wrong. B.P stands for British Pharmacopeia, the official British reference work setting forth standards of strength and purity of medications. For your effort, however, I will excuse you from next week's test." Feeling like Richard Burton having just offered a stellar performance of *Hamlet,* I bowed my head and curtsied.

"You don't have to be melodramatic, Nanji," Stewart remarked. Melodramatic? What was the meaning of that word? It was such a big word for someone barley 14. Even though I read amply I didn't know its exact meaning. It seemed to suggest mellowness mixed in with the dramatic. That didn't make sense.

Since I had just elicited such a warm laugh from Mr. Stewart, I pushed him to explain. "What does melodramatic mean?" I pointed out that one couldn't be both mellow and full of drama.

Stewart looked at me in mild irritation and pushed his steel-rimmed glasses up his nose. I thought he was about to break into a rendition of "Take me Home, Country Roads," but instead he said, "Go to the library, open the dictionary and look it up. Once you have done that, write me a five page essay on the medical benefits of hydrogen peroxide." Stewart was, of course, punishing my lack of discipline. By kicking me out of class and giving me such a tedious assignment he showed me and the other boys that he was still the boss.

I collected my books, but before I left I asked Stewart if he could sing or play the guitar. The rest of the class knew I was referring to him as John Denver and they erupted. It felt like I had just won an Academy Award. Even though I had to write that silly paper, I was fast gaining a reputation as class clown.

I came to realize that mildly foolish behavior was tolerated by many teachers, especially if one was a relatively decent student. Our physics teacher Mr. Noble once let me off for a major violation. Noble had an unfortunately large overbite and a subsequent tendency to spray spit at those in the front row. This was priceless fodder for humor and I could do no less than imitate him as I would any well known cartoon character. One morning Noble caught me in the act of doing my brilliant impersonation of him, of spitting and talking at the same time. Noble, said simply, "That was rude, Nanji" and left it at that.

Not all teachers were gallant as Noble. Mrs. Migue, our Swahili teacher, was at the opposite end of the spectrum and I didn't care if I did well in her class. Many of us Indian boys thought it beneath our station to study Swahili. Our medium of instruction at school was English, so there was no apparent reason to learn more Swahili. Why would I want to better my capability of speaking to servants? We were being taught in the Queen's tongue, and so many of us thought learning advanced Swahili was a sheer waste of our time. Perhaps we could indulge the teachers by learning French, but Swahili wouldn't count toward my "O" Levels. It was like Art or Metalwork, subjects that were a trudge and requirement for school, but with no direct academic reward.

Childhood friend Adil Gilani and I were the back row in our first Swahili class with Mrs. Migue. We were sniggering little boys up to no good and exchanging notes describing the hippo-like size of our new teacher's behind. I wrote, "Big" and Gilani would write back, "Huge". We traded notes for about ten minutes exhausting our knowledge of synonyms for large. One of us even came up with the word, "Gargantuan". So there we were, in the back of the class impressed with ourselves and thinking that we could play this game all term.

It was Mrs. Migue's style to walk slowly around the class, asking the students questions in Swahili and demanding thoughtful answers. In the middle of asking a question to someone way in front of the class, she crept behind our desks in the last row. I was the first to receive a whack from her massive hand. My neck felt like it had come loose, as if a disc had been removed from my spine. Her next blow was to Gilani whose head she hit with the wooden duster she was carrying. Then, dropping the duster and using both her hands, she grabbed each of us by the hair and made us stand up and slapped us some more. Once, twice, thrice;

she was full of rage, and rightly so. We never sat in the back row after that and through the rest of the term behaved like the meek mice we were.

I also never got under Mr. Bentley's skin no matter what I tried. Bentley taught us Maths in the fifth and sixth form, and it was from him I learned the basics of calculus. Bentley had a well-groomed beard, and was well-proportioned with nice arms and especially strong legs. There weren't any women of note at our school for him to impress, but he wore skimpy shorts none the less, perhaps to intimidate us with his soccer player thighs. To earn more respect from the other boys, I tried frequently to bring him down. But Bentley was having none of my lip.

I once asked him, "Mr. Bentley, sir, do you shop for your finely tailored shorts at R.E Bentley?" R.E Bentley was a high-end Nairobi clothing store that for some odd coincidence bore the teacher's last name and his first initial. There was no affiliation between teacher and store, for I knew the store was owned by a Hindu. But I couldn't resist and to prove my worth to the other boys, I launched into enemy territory by commenting on his ultra-tight shorts.

It was a mistake for that day I had a lunch stain on my regimental school tie. Bentley said, "No...I don't shop there, Nanji, but I don't pick my ties from the dustbin either." Score: Bentley 1, Nanji 0.

Another time I foolishly asked if Mr. Bentley if he liked driving a Bentley. "Isn't it an excellent car with lush leather and a purring engine?" I was hoping for some kind of sheepish answer.

Instead Bentley answered rapidly, "I wouldn't know, Nanji. I rather prefer a Rolls-Royce. But since you are so interested in wheels here's a problem for you. Can you calculate the angular deceleration of a wheel traveling at 20 kilometers per hour and stopping to a standstill in 30 meters?"

What? This was a hard problem to solve. I said I didn't know. To which Bentley replied, "Good. Well, find out how to do it. Perhaps you'll learn that before opening your mouth that this is a Maths class, not a fun fair." I was well and truly skewered and had no comeback.

After most of my jokes fell flat or were swatted away by his light-ning quick wit, I realized I had met my match. But Bentley was a true sport. When I left school, he gave me a recommendation for my entry into University that also served as a back-handed compliment. Bentley wrote, "Nanji is occasionally intelligent and one of a kind. His humor should never be underestimated and I have great hopes for him." That was the lovely part about our teachers at Nairobi School. They really cared for their students and were vigilant in turning little boys into men.

In the second form our Geography teacher Mr. Mulindi gave us plenty of reasons to laugh. For no apparent reason he would tip-toe and dance his way around the class like Baryshnikov practicing a difficult routine. He would suddenly stop in mid sentence, pirouette and then point accusingly at one of us, demanding we give him an answer to some question on contour mapping, latitudes or physical topography.

Mulindi also made us read maps as if our manhood depended on our ability to make out railway crossings from swamps. I have been al-ways grateful for that instruction has served me well. I have a certain friend (goes by the name of Harry) who insists on extravagantly ram-bling long hikes or, as I term them, "death marches." Harry gets away with fooling other folks – but not me! I can look at any map, understand the scale and elevation and realize that Harry's suggested journey will take six hours and not the sixty minutes that he might claim. Mulindi's fine teaching, forever ingrained, has been especially useful as I now re-fuse to hike with Harry. This, I am sure, has saved me from numerous muscle strains and unwanted scrapes from falling on granite out of sheer fatigue. (Thank you Mr. Mulindi!)

Mulindi was also incredibly orderly and precise. His script on the black board would make any typographer jealous and also used plenty of color to make his case. Rather than use a flowing hand, Mulindi would attack the blackboard with a seemingly epileptic fit of pointillism, ex-changing blue for pink, and then for yellow to make his pretty pictures. On one occasion, KS Shah, the most elfish looking boy this side of the

Indian Ocean, sniggered loudly when Mulindi punched the board hard causing a piece of chalk to fly and land on a student's desk.

Mulindi wasn't happy with the interruption by this little boy with puffy cheeks and a guilty looking troll-like face. Having just colored a portion of the blackboard to signify a volcano or a different country (I forget which), Mulindi choreographed his trademark pirouette, aimed at KS and hit him on the forehead with the remaining pink stub of chalk. Still standing tall on his tiptoes, Mulindi then ordered KS to "March out of Class." But his command wasn't pronounced March as in the month. Instead Mulindi resorted to the traditional African pronunciation, "marsh".

KS, a little tyke and not one to go down without a fight, asked, "Is there a marsh outside of class?" Is that part of our geography lesson, sir? Mulindi narrowed his eyes, his elegant facial bones hardening into a brittle but concrete resolve. All of us knew he was going to crack, the mystery was how?

Mulindi did not disappoint. He did a double pirouette like the little dancing girl on an antique clock, stood on his tip toes and held this position for a few seconds. Then slowly lifting his arm into a straight arrow, imitating an archer from the Middle Ages, he pointed his finger at KS and barked, "Leave now!" KS knew his time was up and we knew we had witnessed a performance worthy of the Kirov.

For some odd, perhaps even genetic reason, the use of Bantu languages from birth results in an inability for most Africans to pronounce certain English words. But it wasn't just the Africans who had a difficulty in recreating an Oxbridge accent. We Indians had a similar handicap with consonants formed by the letter V and W. And the Japanese, I found out years later, routinely replace the sound of "R" with an "L", resulting in apologies that sound like a desperate search for "Solly".

To make us into worthy users of the exalted language Mr. Keon, our very white English teacher in the first form, insisted on us memorizing a list of common pronunciation errors he had heard while in Kenya. He wrote the following on the board:

Bread __not__ Blade
English __not__ Engrish
Have __not__ Hayw (for the Indians)
That's it __not__ Thazzit
River Road __not__ Limba Load
and Keon's all time favorite: Screwdriver __not__ Schoolodailaba

Keon was a gay, gay man in the best sense of the word and taught both French and English. A rumor floated in school that Keon had one of his testicles shot off by a German marksman in WW II. But when we asked him if had suffered any injuries during the war, Keon was too much of a gentleman to show us if the rumor had actual merit. Keon had spent much of the war undercover in France helping the French resistance and told us some amazing stories of escapes, the joy of living in Provence, the magic of flaky croissants, and the sheer delight of frog legs. Keon said frogs tasted like chicken. We thought he was out of his mind, but with his erudite renditions he nonetheless made us love France from several thousand miles away.

Movies and Love

*M*ovies, as most young and old kids will attest, are magic. Exploring and digging up vast continents of emotion – fear, love, admiration, and, most importantly, laughter – movies are the invention of the century. Who needs penicillin or the motor car? I'd rather trade a tense thriller for the light bulb or a bread slicer any day. But then without light bulbs, we wouldn't have movies, and without a bread slicer, how would I dunk the perfectly sliced soft squares from "Elliott's Bakery" in milk? What a conundrum it was deciding the best from the best! So many worthy things had been invented since George Stephenson's "Rocket"; airplanes, the flushable toilet or the outright gaudiness of the nuclear bomb. But time after time, as I compared the breakthroughs made since the industrial revolution, moving pictures with sound stayed on top of my list of best gizmos ever made.

My buddy with whom I saw "flicks" was Cousin Aleem. Yes, that same boy who could be a sadist, but we were buddies and had fun together. Our cinema halls of choice were the 20th Century Fox near the "Coffee

House" frequented by coffee connoisseurs, and Kenya Cinema, next to the American Embassy. Both were grand, cavernous entities with huge velvet curtains and plush seating arranged as "Stalls", "Circle" and "Royal Circle." In truth any seat was fine once a movie started, but being up high in the Circle section was our favorite. We felt more adult.

Seats were assigned by row and number. Festival seating would have been an ill mannered anathema to our British forbearers who brought moving pictures to Kenya. When we knew of an imminent and well-publicized movie opening, we would take the bus on Saturday morning to the city centre and head to the "advance purchases" booth to claim our prize. Our seats guaranteed, we would return home for lunch, and at 2 PM return back to the city on the bus for the 3 PM matinee. For some years this was a well established routine for Aleem and me. There were plenty of movies to see across the several theatres. If our favorite theatres were playing something we didn't like such as *Last Tango in Paris* or *Doctor Zhivago*, we could catch shows at the Cameo, Liberty, Odeon, Embassy, Metropole, Globe or Majestic. The quality and types of movies at these other temples of fantasy varied. Cameo showed second run movies, while Odeon always seemed to play *The Ten Commandments* or some other devotional Christian story. The Majestik, conveniently housed next to a couple of cheap brothels, was dedicated to soft porn that didn't interest us until we were fourteen. The Embassy or Globe showed Indian Bollywood movies with their incessant litany of songs that broke plot continuity at exactly the wrong time. With Liberty Cinema and Metropole way out in the suburbs of Pangani and Hurlingham, it was natural that the Kenya Cinema and 20th Century Fox became our favorites.

If there was a movie I desperately wanted to see at Metropole, Mummy would haul us over to Hurlingham in her Green VW bug. The drive to the rich, mostly white suburb was dotted with pretty houses and an extraordinary colorful set of fauna and flora. Mummy enjoyed these excursions because I think they gave back a sense of freedom or wanderlust, or simply allowed her to appreciate Nairobi's beauty. After the movie, Mummy would drive us home, happy to see the lit smiles on our faces, a direct result of the magic of movies. On the way back we would often stop at Westland's Dairy Den, where a soft vanilla ice cream cone laid waiting for me to ambush it. It would still be Saturday evening, which meant another day without school followed. We were also going home where the TV breathlessly waited to be switched on. These outings weren't a type of fool's paradise; they were a window into mine.

My love of movies began in primary school where they were shown at the end each term. To not overrun our school's assembly hall the teachers decided to run three showings of the same movie. It was best to be in the first lot, since the plot and juicy scenes would be revealed by the first wave of kids. I hated kids who spoiled the fun of surprise, of not knowing what would happen next. Even more important, the first viewing allowed one a chance to view the movie without interruptions.

Our school projector had the tenor of a patient riddled with the flu. After the first showing it would get tired and sometimes break down, briefly halting the shows before it was administered some kind of life-support. By the third showing, we knew that the projector had very little left in reserve and crashes would be frequent. But even these interrupted showings were special. As kids, we had finished a semester of hard work or daydreaming in class and our rewards were a movie and a month off from school.

The movies chosen for us were those that elicited our howls: Laurel and Hardy, Charlie Chaplin, the Three Stooges and Abbott and Costello. Our school only had access to only a handful of prints, so the movies would be recycled every few terms. This allowed Aleem to perfect mimicry of the many scenes where Moe had his way with Larry and Curly. Although I wasn't fat or bald, I was goofy, clumsy and prone to mishap. And as we relived the scenes we saw on the screen, Aleem naturally assumed the role of the sadistic Moe. Gilani with his lovely locks was deemed Larry, while I became Curly. And so I was the recipient of many two-fingered pokes to the eyes and swipes with paper bags filled with flour. I took this punishment all in good stride; at the end of the day the Three Stooges always went about their mad-hatter ways as a team.

When I was 15 or so a new cinema was opened by the Kenya Film Council (KFC), a state-run film distribution company. This cinema, as the press announced it, would have the latest technology, sound and extra-plush seats. The owners held a competition in the paper to name it; the winner would get two free movie passes for a year. Aleem and I immediately went to my trusty Encyclopedia Britannica dictionary to see how we might come up with the winning name. We divided our possible selections into adjectives that described the grandeur of movies and or names we thought outshined names of existing cinemas. We came with some interesting names, "Spectroscope,", "Far-out," "Shaboom," "Olympia," "Imperial," and "Bazooka," and submitted these and others as individual entries.

To compete, one had to fill out a form printed in that day's edition of the *Daily Nation* newspaper. By then we were in high school and somewhat inebriated with our blossoming brains. As smarty pants we realized that the number of entries could not exceed the print run of the newspaper on that particular day. So we scoured our compound and elsewhere for copies of that issue, and eventually submitted twenty entries. Since we had both quantity and quality, we knew we had the inside track on the free tickets.

We lost. The eventual winner of the naming contest was a six-year-old boy, who thought of the ultra-bland name "Nairobi Cinema". This was a healthy dose of adult idiocy. The name, we now knew, was chosen to reflect the inventiveness of executives running movie companies. To this day I harbor a deep-seated anger aimed at these brainless suits for releasing unpalatably, unimaginative bad movies to our sacred halls.

The oddest movie I saw released by these numb nuts focused entirely on "marbles falling on steps." The dialogue was sparse and incoherent with endless flashback scenes of marbles spilling everywhere. I did not consider these scenes to constitute a meaningful story. So whenever Aleem and I came out of the movies we had just seen, we discussed the merits of the movies on the "marbles" scale. An excellent movie was designated as "no marbles"; while artistic nonsense was simply flagged as "that movie was the marbles." Those movies that fell in between had, like steaks, varied amount of marbling. It was all very silly but highly amusing to us juveniles. Pretty soon, we found ourselves telling any fool that they had marbles in their head. We also convinced ourselves that we had contributed significantly to the science of movie rating and so we should get free passes. We wrote to the KFC suggesting our rating system in the hopes of currying favor and getting free tickets. But, as I have mentioned, movie execs are born dumb, and they didn't respond.

Girls were a definite reason to go to the movies. If a boy took a pretty girl to the movies, it meant he was smitten and they were going steady. This was a big deal especially as we got older. Having a girlfriend at 15 or 16 meant several clear things: Your friends couldn't label you as a homo, you were almost certain to get kissed and you were more of a man than the other pretenders around you. I don't know if this is gorilla or monkey behavior, but I guessed it had something to with evolution. So rather than show off my brawn by directly snaring a girl, I decided to use a little brain.

After Mummy passed, my heretofore dastardly sister, Ferry, and I became closer, even pals. (Yes, very strange). Perhaps the biggest reason for such a turnaround, was because I was now seriously interested in girls. Ferry as a popular girl had access to plenty of these important assets. Indeed, I knew that an alliance with big sister, despite the crateload of self doubt that hung around my neck, would allow me to score on the still pristine turf of romance.

I couldn't think of anything better than to fall in love, hold hands in a park, and kiss incessantly. Sex was out of the picture because we were too modest. It was unbecoming to defile a young Ismaili girl. She would attain the stamp of being "used," and we simply couldn't allow that moniker to be applied to our own girlfriends. So the unwritten ethos of Ismaili dating was that unless you were bound to married in the next year or so, you couldn't do the dirty deed with your girlfriend. Fine, who wanted sex, anyway? That's what the right hand was for. But for God sakes, one couldn't kiss a pillow forever could one? (My advice to any aspiring teenage Don Juan: before attempting any first kiss on the mouth, one should train for a solid month on soft pillows).

Ferry's popularity in high school and at mosque, meant that other girls crowded around her as if she was Queen Bee. As my ordained lookout for girlfriend possibilities, Ferry was the de facto chair of my girlfriend selection committee. Azee, an Olive-Oyl look alike, was an immediate choice for Ferry, but she was ultra-shy. With my own fears of getting rejected, kissing Azee might take another decade or so. Kuku, the second candidate Ferry suggested, was gorgeous. But being two years younger, I surmised she wouldn't know how to kiss. The real reason for my rejecting her was my utter lack of confidence to reach for the brass ring. Kuku would have been a real catch but I knew I needed to set my sights much lower.

Ferry persisted mostly out of my frustration for rejecting her fine picks. One Friday she announced that she and a gaggle of girls were going to the movies that Saturday. More so, she had bought me a ticket and that I would sit next to Zelia. "It's been arranged," Ferry said with finality. "She goes to my high school and is two years behind. She's perfect."

I protested vehemently. Who was this Zelia girl? What did Ferry know about perfection anyway? I had never laid eyes on my future love. She could be unappetizingly fat or have a face full of acne. How dare Ferry arrange a date without letting me first look at the merchandise? Secretly, I was thrilled and I agreed to go.

I began the morning with long preparations of what not to wear. I couldn't appear as too stiff, e.g. in a suit and tie, or dowdy with a grandma-like sweater. I opted for a bit of flash – my new light-grey crimplene bell-bottoms, worn only once previously, and a dark blue Rael Brook Shirt. I finished my look with my platform shoes. These were a size too small and pinched, but I had got them for a song at a clearance sale at the African Boot Company. I was going for the whole nine yards.

That afternoon, we were dropped off by Pops who appreciated the fact that I was pleased to chaperone my sister. Shireen, Aisha and a couple of other girls were already there. In this party was this short Goan beauty with a moon face and big, expressive dark eyes. She was Zelia and I was terrified. Ferry introduced us, and I was as sheepish as a one-legged mouse. I ended up sitting next to Zelia, but was frozen. I agonized how to make the first move but we had barely said a few words to each other. I summoned all the reserve I had and asked her if she wanted any popcorn. Zelia politely refused (Dang! – a first sign that things were not going well!) My heart was racing as the first quarter of the movie passed. Finally I relented from the pressure. I walked away and waited outside until the movie ended. But I had had my first date and several witnesses who could attest to my accomplishment. Now I could face up to any taunting by the other boys. At school I boasted exquisitely about my date, but when Karim Daya (Kydo) asked me I f I had kissed her, I couldn't be caught in a lie or else I would be perennially flagged as a homo. It turned out that Kydo's own girlfriend and Zelia were pals. Indeed, a lie here could have a drastically poor outcome. Instead, I told Kydo, that "I didn't fancy her." Zelia and I never went out again; so much for brain over brawn.

As I got older, I got bolder. One particular time, Aleem wasn't around and I went to the movies by myself on the spur of the moment. I was in the ticket line when I ran into my buddy, Lalji. He was on a date with a girl, who had brought her own sister as a chaperone. He asked me to buy three tickets for him and so we sat in the same row and next to each other, with Lalji and me flanking the two girls. I sat next to Hamida, the chaperone. The most striking thing about this girl was her very large nose in the shape of a parrot's beak. Since I had the same type of nose, only slightly smaller, I was somewhat repelled by her. But I did notice the smooth skin, the supple breasts and her lovely teeth and hair, and while I didn't want her to be my girlfriend, my young hormones were urging me on to conquer.

By the time the lights dimmed for the main movie, I made sure our elbows began to touch. I could feel her heat and wanted more of it. So I pressed ever so softly against her flesh, as if baiting her to press back. Hamida responded with ever more slight pressure. This game continued until I found my hand over hers. She left it there and so I started stroking it casually. She opened up her palm and my own fell into it like a glove. This was the first time I had ever touched a woman in a romantic way. My heart raced as I thought of what to do next. What I really wanted to do was kiss this young little beauty (albeit with a honker of a nose) but it would have been awkward grabbing her head and planting my face in it. What if I missed my target in the dark and our two big noses touched? That would be embarrassing beyond belief.

Instead we held hands for a while, but as my erection grew, I grew more aggressive. I casually began stroking her thigh. She did not object. With my hormones about to explode, I continued my reconnaissance mission of her topography. By folding my arms, I could reach for her nubile breasts without anyone noticing, and so I did. Again she did not object. My first breast! Wow! I pressed it like it was dough of some kind. Hmm... Interesting, and soft, but not entirely satisfying.

What I wanted to do was cream in my pants, but that would have created a mess, so I refrained from touching myself. As I got more excited, I reached for her fly but she stopped me, and put my hand back on her breast. She was telling me I could go to second base but not to third. That was fine with me, I wasn't rejected outright. Besides I wouldn't know how to continue if I reached third base anyway. Yet I had scored my first breast, which I thought was better than kissing.

Hamida and I never ended up sharing a kiss. She followed me a couple of times in the mosque compound, thinking I would talk to her and consummate our kiss. But facing up to her nose, was a struggle for me. It was a promontory I was unwilling to scale. My first kiss would have to come later. But the Hamida experience was revelatory: I had found that men are guided by their weenies, and not their heart.

Although Papa was or seemed to be constantly annoyed at me, we formed a decent pair of moviegoers. I knew I was the no-good skinny son and a burden on his popular image of being a handsome, expert tennis player, and generous, funny guy. So I surmised incorrectly that he took me to the movies only because Mummy must have forced him. Perhaps some element of male bonding was required for me to cut off the apron strings to Mummy that I clutched so tightly. Pops dedication to spending time with me, was his penance for being the house grouch.

It was the best, being Mama's boy but I loved going to the movies with Pops. When I was about six or seven, we would go the Saturday morning shows at Liberty cinema to see spaghetti westerns or great works of myth like Hercules and Samson. Pops adored Alan Ladd, and John Wayne. His notion of the great United States (and therefore mine as well) was based on indomitable spirit of folks in the Wild West.

On rare occasion, we went to movies that I wanted to watch such as *The Love Bug* or *Doctor Doolittle.* But by the time I was ten, Pops thought I was cool enough to watch tough-guy movies starring Charles Bronson or Clint Eastwood. In fact, experiencing a "guy movie" with Pops before any of my other friends was a boost to my self-worth and confidence. I will always be grateful to Pops for those times even though he had annoying habit of sneaking a beer during the intermission. As the projectionists changed film reels, Pops would slip to the bar, and I would tag along waiting impatiently while he enjoyed his Tusker or Pilsner. Because of his imbibing, we would often miss the first minute or so of the movie after the break.

Sometimes he would have two beers, and that really perturbed me since I knew I was now going to miss several minutes of the movie. I'd put up a mild plea to get back into the theatre, but then Pops was the boss, and I had no power. God forbid that I'd make enough of a fuss to incite his dark side. Going to the movies with him was a clear sign to me that I was indeed his son and at least I should be grateful for that. The fathers of most of my friends treated their young sons exclusively as a mother's domain. In our flats it was rare to see a father and son doing something together, except for eating or dishing out criticism.

So I knew there was no need to incite Pops' wrath especially after two beers, when altered brain chemistry begins to remove inhibitory behavior. For all I knew, he would put stop our movie going habits. Worse still he could launch into one of his trademark lectures on the importance of education, respecting one's elders, or the merits of proper table manners. Looking back I realize that Papa's way of loving me was to make me feel like a guy, and a well-mannered one at that. So thank you Pops, annoyances notwithstanding.

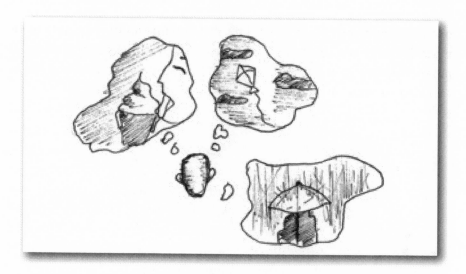

Hobbies

*H*obbies, I am told by the very wise, are activities you love and keep doing from childhood till death. One doesn't simply start a "hobby" and then retreat from it because the interest has waned. That endeavor should never been a hobby in the first place. If that supposition is true then I have only had one hobby – reading.

Everything else I did to amuse myself, or impress girls or my buddies, cannot be classified as a hobby, but more a sheer waste of time, resources and brain synapses. I should start with the complete absurd: my desire to be a black belt in karate. I blame for this the mass hysteria caused by the release of the movie *Enter the Dragon*, starring Bruce Lee. As soon as it opened in Cameo Cinema, every idiot boy I knew now wanted to be as good as Bruce Lee. For those who don't make monstrous mistakes you will not be aware of a venerable scale to classify idiocy; ranging from plain silliness to balls-out insanity. Developed by a high priestess of stupidity – (probably someone such as my sister Ferry) – the scale goes from 1 to 10. A score of 1 denotes only mild delusion. A score of 10 on the other hand suggests that you must be taken immediately to the mental hospital, be placed in chains, given electronic shock therapy, and pumped full of Thorazine.

Well, my trying to be master Kung-Fu artist should have placed me on the upper end of the scale. What was I thinking? Here I was, the skinniest runt in the world with absolutely no flexibility or balance, and I thought I would be the next Bruce Lee?

But what the hey! I joined a dojo in downtown Nairobi and made Mummy purchase for me, at significant expense, a karate outfit or "gi". She drew the line at nunchuks – a deadly weapon of two billy clubs joined by a metal chain. But that loss was okay. I'd figure out a way get a pair eventually. So now I was destined to be the next Karate Kid with my own Sensei, a gi, and a fully paid year-long membership to the dojo.

Our classes began with serious stretching exercises. What? I didn't come to do yoga; I came to be trained as a fighter.

Not carrying the Gumby gene I had a hard time with most stretches, and found myself embarrassed by boys who could scratch their ears with their toes. But I pressed on, and soon I was learning all about Kata 1 and Kata 2, specific movements in karate. There would be no physical contact until we had mastered these Katas. Well gosh-darn-it, I wanted to show how I could floor someone with one forward kick. Couldn't the Sensei make an exception and let me spar? The answer was no. I had to learn the Katas. So over the next few weeks I practiced at home in front of the mirror with little sister Rozy as audience and silent coach.

Each student then took a test to demonstrate the correct technique and pattern on the Katas. With Rozy's admiration of me, I passed and could now begin sparring the following week. My first opponent was a small kid with the bearing of a rodent. I knew I could beat the crap out of him. We bowed to each other and began our contest in earnest. I tried a Maigeri (forward front kick), but was brushed aside easily. Then, with the ferocity of a rabid hyena, my opponent gave me a quick punch to the gut followed by a side kick to the kidneys. I collapsed into a heap, not realizing till then that that such pain was even possible. I was sent home to recuperate. I never returned to the dojo ending my budding career as a Ninja assassin.

I squarely blame my first form classmate Thanawalla for duping me into another sinkhole of a hobby. Thanawalla blinked his eyes constantly as if trying to remove a bothersome gnat's wing or grain of sand. For this and other reasons, such as never wearing a pullover despite some freezing temperatures in the Kenya Highlands, he was an odd duck and didn't have many friends. Early in high school I took it upon myself to model myself as a savior of lost souls. This way, I thought with classic misguided brilliance, I wouldn't be targeted by cruel and sadistic boys as one. I felt was very much like Lady Liberty welcoming the tired, worn out, and miserable to America. Except I wasn't in America and gullible folk like me had no business helping someone who would turn about to be a devious first former.

Thanawalla didn't really care if he was stranger than any weirdo Jim Morrison of the Doors might have seen. What he wanted to do is make me look like a fool just because he could. (This annoying pattern of helping deviant maniacs I repeat ceaselessly. I must carry the genes that lead to milky proteins in the brain and which clouds my reasoning).

Anyway, Thanawalla told me had had just begun a correspondence course in "Computer Electronics." He said that everyone would be using computers one day, and that I should get on the inside track by following him. The inside track on computers! Now that was forward thinking! The course would involve some fairly heavy physics, materials science and college math but he reasoned we were more than capable of learning this advanced stuff. Besides by the time I had finished the course in a couple of years, I would be smarter than any degree holding electronics engineer. I soon floated into visions as a super-successful computer inventor replete with a red sports car, plenty of adoring girls, and a house in some expensive suburb.

Thanawalla told me how to reach the school in the U.S. and I still remember the address. For a full year I sent monthly bank drafts of 110 shillings, or $ 15 to:

National Technical Schools
4000 South Figueroa Drive
Los Angeles, CA. 90037.

In return for this sizable bit of money, I'd get my courses mailed to me as well as a series of "Heathkits" to build my own computer. So far, so good and I soon received my first Heathkit and lessons composing the first module.

The first Heathkit which was a voltmeter disguised as a bunch of discrete capacitors, transistors, plastic parts, and a circuit board. Since I would need this device for testing various future components and circuits I pored over the instructions and began immediate assembly. The instructions also required that I buy a soldering gun and solder wire. So there was a bit more expense, but Mummy thought it was all for a good cause. On the following Saturday we went to an electrical store and bought the tools. I assembled the voltmeter following the instructions almost to a tee. I say almost because I managed to make a mess with the soldering iron and created several shorts on the circuit board. I had fried the device beyond repair before it had even worked. Lesson to budding hobbyists: almost is not equal to exact.

Well, I could always get a replacement voltmeter so I began to plough through the lessons of the first module. I quickly found out that all this nonsense about rectifiers, junction diodes and bipolar transistors was hard to comprehend. I was ignominiously lost by lesson four and I still had 96 more lessons to complete. So I did the rational thing. I gave up on the entire project blaming my failure on indeterminate technical difficulties. Thanawalla then told me that he too had stopped studying before I had even begun making my monthly payments. He burst out laughing as my cheeks and ears flamed red. I wanted to strangle him, but he was bigger than me and I did nothing. Once again, in my exalted career as performing clown I had seized the prize for embarrassment-supreme. Evil Thanawalla had simply wanted to take me down by making me look like an accomplished fool. He was successful.

Medicine Cabinet

*I*ndians have a strange way with medicines. Many strictly follow the Ayurvedic way of their ancestors. Others follow purely modern Western medicine, and some dabble in both to keep their bowels moving and their breath fresh. Ayurveda uses a system of analysis and physical examination done by observation to ascertain one's original nature and current imbalances. A diet and health plan is then given to the sick individual by an Ayurvedic specialist needed to correct any imbalance.

"Medical License? Bah! ... Waste of time!" my Grandma Fatu would exclaim in her broken English. She was a self proclaimed Ayurvedic specialist, which in normal circumstances would perhaps be OK – unless of course if you were one of her young grandchildren.

We loved Mombasa, where Fatu lived with my Uncle and his wife and three fun loving cousins. Mombasa had the relaxed air of a mellow, cosmopolitan and historical beach town. It was perfect for a holiday – no parental supervision, an aunt and uncle who spoiled you, historical intrigue, an ample supply of sweet coconuts, and of course miles and miles of perfect beach. There were narrow alleys, hundreds of years old, where slaves were once traded and white plastered walls layered by time whispered haunting stories at you. Mombasa also had the impressive Fort Jesus built in the 1500's by Vasco da Gama and the Portuguese as their last Africa port of call before sailing off to India in search of spices and silks. Mombasa was my idea of paradise, but it could only become such after I had endured the first day of forced medical treatment.

We weren't sick when my sisters Ferry, Rozy and I arrived in Mombasa. But with the first look at me Grandma Fatu knew I had several ills that must be treated. Mummy had said Granny Fatu's Ayurvedic knowledge was supreme and there was to be no resisting anything she offered. Fatu's diagnosis for me was the same every year; that I was constipated, had a weak constitution and poor eyesight, and that as an adult I would suffer from impotence if I wasn't treated early and often. As soon as we arrived from the railway station, Grandma Fatu would grab my hand with ferocity and lead me to her room where she stashed a variety of herbs, ointments, potions and other weird items. Years later, when observing the strange happenstances in the drug bazaars of Amsterdam, I noticed the clear parallel. Grandma Fatu was trying to change my brain chemistry and body into something that resembled strength, good manners and to be prepared for the future. The regimen I was forced to take was a four-course affair. All of it had to be taken on the first day else, I was summarily told, no beach time or my favorite coconut water.

The first item I was to take to correct my imbalance was a white, vile substance that coated my mouth with a taste that made me want to vomit. This was, Grandma Fatu said, needed to "clear my bowels from all the junk I had been eating at school".

Next she took her brass pestle and mortar and crushed some brown seeds and mixed them with plain yogurt and made me swallow half a glass of this contemptible suspension. As a kid I hated yogurt which I thought was sour and an insult to cows forced to give up their sweet, creamy milk. After adding the bitter seeds she called the resulting mixture "Fakhi" and stressed that this would improve my ailing liver and kidneys. All I knew was that I was already plenty fucked, and this was still only the second course.

Next I had to drink a whole glass of fresh carrot juice to clear my supposedly rheumy eyes. This wasn't too bad, but when it reacted with the Fakhi I had just imbibed, I would let out a smelly burp that, yes again, made me want to puke. Fatu wasn't done yet. She had this grey coarse powder mixture that she mixed with water; another mixture in which appeared to float dead insect heads. After that the torture would be over. However, if I vomited during any of these proceedings, which I once did, I would have to repeat the entire feast. Grandma Fatu, born in the Island of Zanzibar, and having lived her entire life on Africa's East Coast was significantly influenced by the coastal Arabs. Since the ninth or tenth century, Arabs had coming to the coast on their "dhows" or peculiar sailing vessels to trade with the coast. What they wanted was ivory, rhino horn (an ancient form of Viagra), and docile black folk who made for the best slaves. Through the centuries many Arabs didn't take the prevailing winds back home and instead made Africa home lured by a moderate tropical climate and ample-breasted, elegant Bantu women. What was there not to like? The Arabs made plenty of babies with the local wenches and a new type of African was born. These new breed of "Swahili Arabs" dipped into their respective cultures to create a unique mixture of Bantu dialects and Arabic.

From the deserts, Arabs also imported with them their mythology of Djinns (Genies), supernatural creatures who depending on whim can create havoc to humanity or conversely provide valuable service. Everyone on the Coast was terrified of these Djinns, with their amazing powers capable of spreading disease and insanity. One did not mess with Djinns say by pissing on a mango tree at night or otherwise behaving like idiots. Add to this the myths of the Bantu passed on down by witchdoctors and medicine men, and the coast was teeming with bad ghosts lurking at every corner. Grandma Fatu understood the Djinns all too well and we thought even knew some of them on a first name basis.

In no uncertain terms, we were told that major misbehavior could mean a long sentence in the close proximity of one of these wicked creatures.

Well it turned out lucky for Fatu that sister Ferry had recurring bouts of constipation and acne. To help alleviate this tragedy on Ferry's pretty face and to restore her bowel movements, Fatu first tried her bunch of odd Ayurvedic potions. When this first approach didn't work, Fatu moved on to Plan B.

Grandma Fatu said that the stubbornness of the ailments and their inability to respond to the best of Ayurvedic treatments meant only one thing: that Ferry was possessed by a mischievous Djinn. This devil, Grandma Fatu told us with conviction at the dining table, was unlikely to leave the lovely confines of a young, pretty girl without some drastic action. Fatu also said she would need help in the procedure and so she asked her sister Kathi, who lived in Nairobi at the time, to assist. There was never any countermanding of anything if Fatu believed it was vital to family health, so Mummy and Pops quietly acquiesced. The "procedure" was to take place on a Saturday afternoon. I don't know why Saturday afternoon, perhaps the Djinns went shopping or decided on a ride through the country and so were easier to spot. Or perhaps it was a young Djinn susceptible to injury as little kids are when they are monkeying around out of school. It may also have been the Moon rising over Jupiter, or some such astrological absurdity; another area of Fatu's deep expertise. I asked but was never told.

When the time of the procedure arrived, I was summarily told by Fatu to "go outside and play." What? I wanted to see Ferry cut up like a carcass. Fatu, Kathi and Ferry entered into a bedroom, and shut the door behind them. Even Mummy wasn't allowed to be present. Apparently the procedure was too dangerous for a mother to be there. So Mummy sat outside, waiting. Mummy told me that she knew someone who had risked this procedure when all else had failed. I asked Mummy what was going to occur. Mummy said she didn't know but that Grandma Fatu would be careful with my beloved sister.

I said with a voice full of fake concern, "I hope they don't hurt her too much." I didn't want Ferry to die of course, but I *did* want her to suffer on account of her consistently superior attitude in all aspects of our lives. So Mummy and I sat outside, and after minor pleading she let me view the proceedings through the keyhole.

Fatu and her sister went to work. First they walked methodically near Ferry's bed silently, going from side to side both carrying incense sticks. Presumably this was to anaesthetize the Djinn or smoke him out. Next they started with some low indecipherable Arabic incantations, like some out of tune Benedictine choir. As Ferry lay there still, a cloth over her eyes, the two older ladies, rolled their own eyes in unison, revealing their whites and giving me the creeps. Next they began slapping their hands together and finally both of them briefly placed their heads on Ferry's stomach as if to listen. Ferry screamed as Fatu smacked her stomach, and it was all over.

After a minute or more of waiting, the door opened. Fatu said the Djinn was gone. What no blood, no gore, not even vomit? Soon after, Ferry's acne gradually began to diminish, and her bodily functions came back to normal. It was yet another victory for medicine woman Fatu.

More Medicine

A recount of my ailments or medical issues might imply that my childhood must have been rather dull. I suffered no broken bones and was never hospitalized. I also never had any surgery done to me and didn't develop any communicable diseases like those boys who, for a few shillings, slept with Pande's promiscuous ayah. Yet I had my fair share of scrapes and minor trauma.

To Mummy one of my most problematic ills was my unnerving ability to get spontaneous nose bleeds. For no apparent reason, while reading a book or forcing down my lunch, blood would stream out of my left nostril. Once the vessel blew, my face would quickly become a frightening bloody mess and I thought I was going to die. My overactive imagination contrived that I was radioactive. Like some folk who had suffered through nuclear blasts, I half-believed I was doomed to die from a significant loss of hemoglobin. Mummy was also not sanguine about these unwelcome incidents for as soon as the blood platelets did their thing to clot and stem the flow of red, I'd reach into my nose to pick at a crusty blood booger and repeat the whole process. On a couple of occasions, I lost so much blood Mummy forced me to eat liver to replenish all the lost iron. And I hated liver.

Mummy tried various approaches to stop these scary flows including the classic use of forcing me to look up to the sky or ceiling for hours on end. Yet it was trying to remove the hardened blood snot that always put paid to a recovery. Mummy resorted to an approach suggested by Grandma Fatu and was partially successful. She would burn silk – it had to be pure silk – and made me breathe the fumes. For whatever reason, silk fumes were thought to be good coagulants. I thought it was yet another way Grandma Fatu had devised to clean out my bowels. But the blood flows continued and Mummy couldn't take the frequent recurrences. So I waited in line for several hours to see the Ear, Nose and Throat (ENT) specialist who made a weekly round at the Aga Khan Hospital.

Doctor D'Cruz was a kind-looking bald Goan who looked up my nose; a reflector banded about his head to remove glare. Like so many other doctors, D'Cruz spoke the universal language of Doctorese. He went "hmm, aaah", and then said "I see." Next, he took what looked like a slim soldering iron, turned it on, waited for it to heat up before using it to poke at my insides and burn off some offending flesh. It smelled like a Brazilian barbecue, but then he said with finality, "You are cured." I asked what had been wrong. D'Cruz said a very large blood vessel at the bridge of my nose was the offender, and he had put paid to its bad behavior by grilling it. I finally understood why cows and chicken don't like to be flame-broiled. My nose never bled again, except once after college when I mistakenly snorted a large amount of cocaine thinking it was sugar.

Visiting the doctor that day had another seminal moment. Mummy couldn't take me to the hospital. Something may have been cooking, or she may have had a neighbor visiting seeking solace from supporting a dead-beat husband. So Mummy dispatched my sister Ferry to accompany me on the ten minute walk to the hospital. Being alone together, as brother and sister, sparked off something, and we were laughing hard by the time we arrived at the hospital. For the first time in my life, I didn't see my older sister as some annoying, fire-breathing dragon. Instead Ferry was warm, funny and quite silly. After I got my nose job, I also now knew that my relationship with Ferry had changed forever. Going forward, she would forever be my great friend and companion as well as a clumsy nut with whom I could share the sillier side of my life. All it took for us to bond was some blood.

If there is one person who is more prone to minor mishap than me, it was Ferry. In the annals of childish disaster, one event ranks extraordinarily high. As she was most mornings, Ferry was late catching the bus to school. With her hair already unkempt, her school tie at half-mast, and white socks hitting her ankles, she looked like she had just come *back* from a full day of school rather than just having dressed for it. Ferry also mistakenly thought she was a good athlete. Holding her schoolbag in one hand and a piece of half-eaten toast in the other, she flung herself toward the just departing bus, screaming, "Wait! Wait!" Ferry mistimed her jump and fell face-first into a deep puddle of red African mud. She was now covered from head to toe in wet dirt. But like the trooper she always was, she simply laughed at herself, wiped off whatever she could, leapt once more and went inside the bus.

Getting sick with an inflamed throat was a frequent occurrence for me. My lymph nodes would swell-up painfully, and soon I got tired of it. My friend Khanbhai, in flat #50, told me that he had gone to the hospital for treatment of the same ailment. There they performed an operation to remove one's tonsils. After that surgery Khanbhai said he never had any more throat pain. I was particularly attracted by his tale that one was fed immense amounts of ice cream after the operation. Well that was a call to action for me. I promptly willed myself into illness and asked Mummy to take me to the hospital operating room.

I could almost taste the delicious ice cream but Mummy first took me for a consult to our primary care physician, Dr. R.M. Patel. Well, the short of it was that Mummy believed the ignoramus doctor who said I shouldn't get the tonsils removed, and never should. He told Mummy it was a wasteful operation to perform, and also an unnecessary mutilation of the sacred body. Instead, Dr Patel did something else. He made me remove my pants and proceeded to jab me hard in the buttocks. He said that would cure me provided I came back two days later for one more jab. So no ice cream but two pointed and hurtful pricks later I had saved my tonsils which, I am sure, are thrilled to be alive.

Whenever Mummy thought I was sick but a doctor wasn't needed, she fussed and tended over me a like a finicky orchid. Any sign of blood made her feel that her little darling idiot-boy might die. But blood never really did bother me except if it was coming out of my nose with unwanted abandon. One heroic stand of not breaking out into tears came on a rainy Saturday evening. Lalji and I were hitting a tennis ball along the long high wall guarding the servants' lavatories. With my usual carelessness, I bounded after a ball but didn't see the hulking shape of a large concrete post right next to us. So when my head hit had against the post's very sharp edge, I suffered a long gash that ruptured an important artery bearing a Latin name.

Like the numskull I was, I decided to play on. But Lalji called a halt to our tennis battle, when he saw red everywhere. I went home thinking, I was a boxing champ. The bump with the post did was not painful, but I was bleeding profusely and looked like I had been mauled by a troop of angry baboons. The very silver lining was that I could boast I lost a pint or so of blood yet was strong enough to take my punishment like a prize fighter, that I didn't cry.

Mummy, on the other hand, panicked as she opened the door for me after I rang our front door bell. Now even though I was a mama's boy, any added attention I could get from Mummy, was like being a pig in shit. (Or is the image of a shitting pig?). Porcine references aside, I looked a sorry sight. Mummy went into emergency mode and first washed away the caking blood. Next she applied turmeric – a well known clotting agent for us Indians – and then wrapped my head with a white makeshift bandage from cheesecloth she used for cooking. Then I was "ordered" to sit down in a favorite chair and watch television, while she brought me a grilled cheese sandwich with piping hot tomato soup. These were cool advantages of smashing ones head against a pillar. I had stopped bleeding, but with a two inch gash on my forehead, I debated if I shouldn't get additional treatment from a real doctor. What if her little boy had permanent memory loss? What if he would become insane from hitting his head too hard? These were silly questions that now ran through my mind.

After downing the sandwich and the soup (soft and delicious), I relaxed enough to have a brainwave. I could get stitches! Having a wound that requires a Doctor to sew it and later removing the stitches when healed was a mighty badge of honor amongst us boys. It demonstrated that we were capable of reckless injury, and the fortitude to withstand torture. Lalji was the "king" of surgery and he sported several scars on his knees and arms to prove his manhood. Even flaky, scaredy-cat Khanbhai often showed off a scar caused by the removal of his bloated appendix. I had no proof I was a man, unless I stripped naked and displayed my nuts. Here was an opportunity to seize.

In desperate need of approval by my mates, I opened the bandage on my head to re-examine the cut in the mirror by the sink. The bright yellow of the turmeric and the red of the dried blood on my brown skin made me look like a crazed Apache.

I thought this was a very cool look and was briefly enchanted with the thought of leaving off the bandage. But what I really wanted was stitches. Right then, Mummy emerged from the kitchen, horrified. "Chokra! What are you doing?" she squawked.

I said, "I think I need stitches Mummy".

"No, you don't, darling. That would be too painful for you."

"That's precisely the point," I wanted to say. But I wavered easily, being the wimp that I was, and instead agreed, "Yes I think the cut has closed" and let her reapply the bandage. The bump on my head still exists. For years it was not noticeable because of my mass of hair just above it. But as my hairline receded over the years, it now stands exposed like an odd ridge, reminding me of the clotting power of turmeric, the way Mummy fussed over me, and yet another missed opportunity to prove I really was male.

My only other significant injury occurred riding my bike. I had just learned how to ride "hands-free" and thought I could turn a sharp corner without placing my hand on handlebars. I was, of course, wrong, and careened into a low concrete rise. My glasses flew off and I feel to the tarmac scraping my knee. I was lucky and the wound was superficial. Over the years this scar has shaped into the island of Madagascar, off the African coast. Now whenever I need a bit of nostalgia to warm me as I trudge through the cold East Coast winter, I simply have to look at my scar and I am transported to Africa to bask with lemurs.

My Hindu Boys

I credit my Hindu boys for dragging me out of my private closet. I was 16 and I really liked girls by now, but they terrified me. I had a big nose; I was awkward and I was as skinny as a stick insect. Girls, I had discovered, were gorgeous things of beauty – especially the non-ugly ones – and I couldn't wait to fall in love. But which pretty young thing in her right mind would ever want me? My sister Ferry had tried to set me up with some dates, but I couldn't muster any type of conversation with her choices. As I got older I became even more tongue tied around females. I believed that none of them could see through the veil of my monotonic quiet to reveal a sensitive, funny heart yearning to give it away to the first girl who said boo.

I was also way behind the curve. My classmate, Kydo, already had Alka, a pert little Sunni Muslim girl with lascivious eyes. Damji, although chubby, looked like a catch with his hip dark glasses and fair skin, and probably had even done the dirty deed; he kept talking about the danger of getting crabs at the whorehouse behind the Majestic cinema, so there must have been some truth to his observation. Several younger boys in the flats, including Lalji and Virani, were experimenting with French kissing and boob squeezing. And, Sulu a full two years my junior, used his handsome face to regularly get blow-jobs behind the cricket pavilion next to our mosque. Yet all I wanted to do was hold hands and gaze into someone's eyes who would view me as equally magical. And I was nowhere.

It was all so unfair. I could attribute much of this blame to my spindly physique. If any girl ever saw me naked I knew there was a good chance that she would throw-up.

Then along came my Hindu friends at Nairobi School to save me from ignominy. These six really were a mixture of Jains, Lohanas, and Patels, but I couldn't tell the difference, since none of their mothers ever prepared meat for their lunches. In addition, Diwali was a very big deal to all of them and they weren't too fond of Pakistan even thought they had never been there. From my perspective, it seemed that their all Hindu's families sold shoddy or upscale goods to a rapidly growing Kenyan consumer society. The Hindus were Kenya's mercantile champions, and by the time I hit high school many of these families had untold wealth. A sprinkling of them bought Mercedes' and moved away from communal houses in run-down Ngara to wealthier suburbs like Westlands and Parklands. The exodus soon became a torrent and a competitive spectacle of the Hindus trying to keep up with each other.

Every Hindu family I knew bought huge fancy cars, expensive clothes, and mountains of gold with which they could chain down their mothers and daughters. They also began displaying their wealth by hosting private parties and lavish weddings. As a non-threatening Ismaili, I was initially invited to a few weddings and a number of parties and often for lunch. The primary Hindu ethos, I learned, was that mothers are the most revered but fully dedicated to their men. It was a soft, caring, tight-knit community and I began to like their spicy vegetables, sweet dal and shikand.

As a general rule, the Hindus were nouveau riche and bourgeois. Their educated did not have the uppity class accent and education of many Ismailis who went to university at Loughborough, Oxford, Canada, and London. Instead the Hindus still sent their sons to become doctors and accountants in Bombay or Poona in India. (The daughters, of course, were married off as quickly as possible.) Technically, this allowed me to pose with a chip of superiority for our "foreign" education meant us Ismailis were whiter than the Hindus. (Again a silly fallacy - while I haven't officially checked, our DNA is likely similar to that of the Hindus. Most of us Ismailis in East Africa came from a lineage of Hindus in India who had been converted to Islam in the 19th century).

But I didn't display my built-in Ismaili arrogance at these Hindu functions. I personally had nothing to be arrogant about; I thought I was an ugly wimp. But a few girls, sisters or cousins of my Hindu boys took an instant liking to me. These females I thought were downright gorgeous. It was all very flattering and my confidence surged. I began to hang out more with the Hindu boys looking for more opportunities to interact with these girls.

On Saturday afternoons, one of the Hindu boys would borrow a luxury car from the family pool, and we would go on field trips to discover more of Nairobi's outskirts. While we were merely 16 or 17, young Indian boys bribed their way to a driver's license and so the parents had few qualms on letting us loose. There were no girls on these road trips, but it was how we planned for our Saturday nights.

I enjoyed these planning sessions with these funny, warm group of non-violent boys. It was more my style. Once we went to Ngong Hills on an exploration and civics lesson. It was often reported in the *Daily Nation* that buried in the hills were truckloads full of decapitated bodies belonging to the President's burgeoning group of political enemies. We didn't find any evidence, but then we really weren't desperately looking for any dead Kikuyus or Jaluos. Another time, we went to a dairy outside of Nairobi, where we drank the freshest, unpasteurized milk just because we could. On several other occasions we took trips to the airport to view the spectacle of long-haired, hippies arriving from the U.S. in search of unspoiled Africa, drug-induced nirvana or the savannah. The young men would come with obscenely large, dirty back-packs, unkempt long hair and were unshaven. The ladies wore unflattering, dirty jeans, no make-up, looked chunky and were nowhere close to anything that resembled our view of feminine beauty. We would sit there at the airport laughing as these American dregs looked for public transit to the City. (What were these fools thinking? There was no public transport to the city save for expensive taxis). We surmised that their parents and country didn't want them and so shipped them over to our little paradise with a few bucks in their pockets.

After a Saturday afternoon excursion, there was usually a birthday disco party of a Hindu somewhere to attend that evening. These were relatively secret events, and entrance was by invitation only. The docile Hindus parents did not want the riff-raff of Muslim boys or Sikhs coming close to their beloved girls. But since I tagged along with my Hindu boys, I was admitted to all such events.

It was there I first met Devia, a thin beauty with the face of an Indian movie actress in a long, shimmering blue maxi-gown. We spoke about school for a minute and then did a couple of fast numbers on the dance floor when the strobes went out and the lights fully dimmed. Devia reached hesitantly for my waist and we began to slow dance. I became bolder and held her closer. She melted into me like the finest of Swiss chocolate. We spent the night dancing, not talking, and then held hands as we walked off the floor. It was late and her ride was leaving. We looked at each other in earnest, and I was in love.

Since Devia was a friend of a friend of a friend, I had no way of getting in touch with her. My Hindu boys told me where she lived but that was all they could do. They couldn't risk trouble with their elders by arranging for her to meet with an Ismaili. So for three Sundays I walked the three miles to her family's large bungalow and stalked her. She only saw me only once on these love pilgrimages. I recall standing there like an eager dolt in the best clothes I had. She smiled and waved from afar and promptly went back to the sanctuary or prison that was her home. I never saw Devia again, but I had loved and now could move on with the knowledge that a girl – a real live girl – had liked me.

In our last two years of high school, the barriers between us various types of Indians broke down. There were only a handful of us remaining. Most Indians who had joined us in the first form had gone off to England, to St. Mary's, the predominantly white high school in the valley, or simply didn't make the grade for the final two years.

After four years of high school every Kenyan student sat for a national examination. To continue the next two years at Nairobi School one had to do well on this exam or be forced to leave. Spots in form five and six at all good schools were very tight, since they really were weeding programs for university places. The spots vacated by those who didn't make it were awarded to other students throughout Kenya who had done well on the exams.

Only a handful Indians made the cut or wanted to stay at what was now a predominantly black school. Those of us who remained quickly formed a clique. We knew that to survive and have fun all Indians would have to band together. We could have made friends with white or black students in our class but that would have anathema to the way we were raised. So our small cadre of Indians shared recess and lunch and sat apart from others in class.

Crossing a range of religious lines we Indians became fast friends. In our motley crew were five Hindu boys, a Sikh, a new Bohra from Malindi, a couple of Sunni's, a Goan (Catholic Indian) and me. A white skinned Arab, with a large frizzy Afro also briefly joined our group, but left when he felt he wasn't brown enough. We were all good boys and didn't drink or want to drink. Only Salyani among us smoked cigarettes, or so we thought, until I busted Lobo the Goan milling around the city center holding a fag like he was a movie star.

Salyani was a Sunni-Memon and became my best pal. I liked him because he pushed the envelope and everything was a joke to him. He led most of our group discussions that usually ended in howling laughter.

The names in our brotherhood don't mean a thing to anyone but to me they evoke warm memories at the apex of my childhood. So to Rajdev, KS Shah, KJ Shah, KH Shah, Sehmi Singh, Palkhi, Chaudhry, Bhatt, Salyani and Lobo I raise a glass or, if you prefer, a spliff. It was through you that I obtained shelter and finally the confidence and courage to mature.

Early Memories

*M*y earliest vivid memory was of my fourth birthday party in Mombasa. Perhaps my birthday in the first three years wasn't celebrated – or perhaps it was. I don't know and never actually inquired. At that tender age just between oblivious infancy and bawling toddler-hood, what happened before I was actually cognizant of "me" seemed irrelevant. In truth I probably simply thought of myself as just another as another of those bumbling Homo Sapiens, simultaneously committed to the vast destruction of the rain forests and icecaps while protecting cute little polar bear cubs and Bengal tigers.

Hosting the birthday party for me was my aunt Mithi in Mombasa and several rambunctious older cousins. I was there by Mummy's side in the pretty house by Tudor Creek, eagerly awaiting lighting of the candles on the cake, when I said something silly. I don't know what it was – recall I was only four. While what I said this wasn't important, the lifelong repercussions that stemmed from the way I was being laughed at, have scarred me for life. Even at that early age, I knew I was destined to be a clumsy, goofball that everyone would tease. The cruel, angry guffaws all seemed directed at my inherent stupidity. The only person who wasn't laughing was Mummy. The rest of the older folks were like vultures, clawing away at my innards. Feeling ashamed and ridiculed I naturally broke out into tears, as any little munchkin would do, and ran away. I don't remember ever trying the cake.

As the years progress, one realizes that an early childhood trauma such as this could have led to my disdain for chewy foods and an ever present fear of adults. I like some food, but as I have mentioned elsewhere, it was a chore getting anything down my throat. Instead, I needed all the time I could muster into a childhood of discovery; to lose myself in my head as little kids do, to make up worlds, to build fantasies, and tempt the grim reaper by eating grass which I believed to be to poisonous.

The grass eating incident occurred when I was five in our tiny garden with an even tinier patch of lawn. Something inside me, said I would die if I ate grass. I had just learned some elderly person in the flats had just passed, and I thought it would be cool to check out the meaning of death and afterlife. So I began chewing on some cud. But I panicked almost immediately when I realized I didn't *really* want to die. Dying could be forever. All I wanted was a taste of the beyond. What if I didn't come back? The only way I knew I was still alive after munching on a few blades of Kikuyu grass, was to say "Mummy" loudly. If I heard myself saying "Mummy", my tiny little brain would confirm I was alive. Yes, indeed I could hear myself, and I escaped death.

I might not have been so fortunate eating grass from an overly-preened lawn in an American suburb. Since we rarely applied toxins to flora and fauna in Nairobi, I was lucky not to just die but also not to not suffer kidney and liver damage. Not having the likes of "Ortho" or "Roundup" used for killing unwanted weeds, both human and plant, was yet another disadvantage of growing up in Kenya. Couldn't Kenya have nurtured at least one DuPont, Dow or Monsanto to feed us a steady diet of formulated chemicals and make our lives better or worse?

My fear of losing Mummy was, like the desire to taste the afterlife through grass eating experiments, another persistent theme while growing up. The fear still lurks within me to this day, ready to surface and send me bawling; the anxiety coursing through me even though my mother passed on over 30 years ago. Mums are protectors, lovers and providers to little tykes, and I was no exception. It would be rare to spot me not hovering around Mummy's apron. One evening, when I about five or so, and after prayers at the Parklands mosque I was lured away by some smell or the promise of a friend. Terror rose in me like dengue fever as I realized that I had wandered away from Mummy. All I could see around me were a sea of unrecognizable saris and ill-fitting suits. My first reaction was to stand mute like any other five year old; panic-stricken, eyes searching. Then came the first couple of tears and I regained some authority over the fear. But it wasn't over and the next wave of fear hit me quickly. I began sobbing lightly. But that soon gave way to full- throated, balls-out wailing. Everyone could hear me now, except for Mummy. Some of the kind sari-robed ladies tried to comfort me, but I was oblivious – my Mummy, in her bright green frock was missing. Someone had stolen my Mummy!

But then, surely because I was in the mosque, the Angel Gabriel, came down from out of his hiding place, gently made Mummy reappear and hold me close. I was saved and became a full- fledged believer in God, at least for the next week or so. A few years later, as I watched Mummy make my favorite meat pies – a soft covering of mashed potatoes over lightly spiced ground beef – I recounted the story to Mummy. I asked her if my savior was indeed the Angel Gabriel and not one of the nondescript 186,500 prophets, mentioned in the Holy Koran. Mummy smiled and said, "It was the Angel Gabriel, my darling son. He told me not to ever leave you."

On the topic of heaving chests and streaming tears, another bodily function that I first consciously experienced as a tot, was vomiting. I had found a bowl of salty cashew nuts at home, and as any self-respecting toddler would do, I had to eat all 100 or so pieces. When I expunged huge chunks of undigested cashew nuts suspended in a yellow liquid, I thought I was going to die. Mummy thought so too, but Papa, unsympathetic as ever to my plight as a terrified little mama's boy, nonchalantly sat in a dining room chair waiting for this annoying episode to get over.

My first experience of throwing up was fruitful in the long run. Uncannily, I can now control nausea simply by substituting discomfort with the image of my father sitting peacefully while his little son ripped apart his insides. Whenever I have a wave of nausea induced by a dirty rat in the subway or after too many shots of Jack Daniels or Wild Turkey, I simply think of not vomiting on Papa's pretty grey sweater.

A more pleasant memory of my young childhood and Papa was when he said I did a good job at school. Even though we were barely weeds in my first year of primary school, students were ranked each term on how well we did at English and Maths. In my first term ever, my report card duly noted that I was ranked as 40th out of 40 students – that is last. I don't remember Pops saying anything to me after those results, or after the second term when I climbed perceptibly to 25th out of 40. But knowing Pops I'm sure he must have expressed great displeasure.

In the final term of my first year of primary school, I amazed myself and Papa when I ranked first out of forty. This meant I would get the prize for being the best student in my stream that year. But better still, I was temporarily not subject to Pops' long lectures on the merit of a good education. I recall dancing like a dervish with my chum and cousin Aleem for matching his brilliance. (Aleem, also my nemesis, had stood first in all three terms in *his* stream that first year). Pops was tickled, and Mummy was ever so proud. I can still see her kind, gentle face; tears welling on the sides of her soft almond-shaped eyes thinking that her little boy would, after all, be OK.

At age six my first year of primary school also brought me great embarrassment. The worst of these horrific incidents that flushed my cheeks and turned my cauliflower ears red occurred in the school assembly hall. Our principal, Mrs. D'Souza, a prim and proper Goan lady who seemed to have a kind streak, was on the dais imploring us to get our parents to pay our school fees on time. She said it was very important that we did that else the school would not run well. Sensing an opportunity to demonstrate what a goody-two shoes I was, I shouted loud enough for the entire school to hear "But Mrs. D'Souza I have paid my fees."

Mrs. D' Souza, did what any human would do, she laughed out loud at the silliness of my remark and said, "Of course, I wasn't talking about you, funny little boy." The entire school erupted into a wail of high pitched giggles and shrieks. I felt the walls shake from the echoes of laughter, a sharp pain in my chest and sensed the blood rushing, coloring my ears bright red. I could not have been more embarrassed if I was naked. I sought refuge in my older sister, Ferry, and went looking for her. But Ferry avoided me studiously that day; she wouldn't have anything to do with a nincompoop of a little brother.

Alternating between good and bad memories, presents, I believe, a reasonable balance of my wonderfully idyllic but tortured childhood. One Saturday afternoon after a family lunch at my Uncle Badru's house to celebrate Eid, six of the young teens and adults sat down to play Monopoly. At seven I was mesmerized by the various strategies employed to build wealth. The older folk were having a blast, ribbing each other but still being immensely competitive as they horse traded properties, passed Go, paid fines and won beauty contests. I knew then that I wanted to be a real estate tycoon as I ogled at the high rents of posh Mayfair, Park Lane, Bond Street and the other "green" districts. But then as I watched my cousin, Mahmoud, make a killing on the "yellows" of Piccadilly Circus, Coventry St., and Leicester Sq. I knew that this was both a game of deep skill and luck.

As the players mortgaged their futures and paid expensive visits to those lucky *and* smart folk with hotels, the opponents whittled down to two. The winner was either to be Pops with his stranglehold on the railroads, and of the "reds" - -Trafalgar Square, Fleet Street and The Strand, or Mahmoud with the "yellows" and utilities. Pops eventually won and I had never been so proud of him. (I could now boast to all my friends – "My Dad can beat up your Dad in Monopoly."). This, of course set me on a path to desire my own Monopoly set, one through which I could learn the intricacies of strategy and take advantage of the nuanced rules.

One early Saturday, as Pops and Mum were sipping on their morning tea, I rushed down the stairs eager to begin my play-day activities with my friends on this non-school day. I was trying to slink out through the back door when Papa busted me and instructed me to go to the "side cupboard," a largish mahogany repository for all kinds of family knick knacks. I asked why? He said, "Just go open it". I looked inside and saw a rectangular shape packet wrapped in brown paper. I knew with instant joy that I was the proud owner of my own Monopoly set. Strict Papa wasn't all bad after all and Mummy transmitted her love for him through her smiling eyes.

Another toy that Papa bought me was a "remote-controlled" space rover. Pops took cousin Aleem and me to "Hobby Centre" near his office by City Hall, and surprised us each with the coolest little gadget known to boys. The battery- operated, remote-controlled device was one I could drive and manipulate. Oh what fun! I imagined showing this off to all my friends and being the envy of all. We got home and Aleem went to his house clutching his gift, while I tore through the wrapping and asked Pops to put in the batteries. Pops duly did this, and I began exploring the lunar surface of our flat. Jumping over a major mountain, in the form of Ferry's shoe, the rover stalled and died. I picked it up, and tried to restart it but to no avail. In a space of a few minutes, I had destroyed something I so desperately desired. Pops was almost violently angry raising his hand but then dropping it in favor of a yelling. To Pops it was yet another classic display of my utter disregard of valuables. The irony of this episode was that Aleem's rover, a duplicate of my own, lasted for over a year. (Foiled again, by that dastardly Aleem!).

One of the few times Mummy yelled at me was also due to my innate stupidity. The rare dressing down by Mummy came on the day of Eid, an important religious occasion. Following centuries of tradition, kids were doled a few shillings by our elder relatives if one cornered them in time. The trick was to find them almost immediately after "Namaz" or the special Eid prayers else the window of giving would be closed. After prayers when the elders began congratulating each other on their devotion to Allah, Aleem and I took off hunting for any older relatives. Since Pops and Aleem's mum, Sultan Aunty, were the youngest of nine siblings, we knew we had plenty of opportunity to score.

Aleem and I did well that year, collecting about five shillings each from several relatives. The money was doled out in currency notes rather than in coins, lending even more prestige to the collected loot. If ever we had money, we kids mostly had this in the form of coins. So Eid was a particularly sweet time; we could feel and see paper currency that was entirely ours. This particular Eid I ended up with about 25 shillings, a small fortune for any six-year-old. (Aleem bested me yet again with his total of 30 shillings, but I was content like Warren Buffet must be when compared to Bill Gates.)

Feeling rich, we decided to splurge part of our new found fortune at the club canteen about a hundred yards away from the mosque. We both ordered a bottle of Coke and a helping of kachoris (deep fried spicy mashed potatoes covered in a floury-egg batter). Our parents did not like us eating this junk or any other street food, but this being Eid we knew we would likely escape without recrimination.

Still burping from the rapid ingestion of gassy Coke and fried contraband we headed back to our parents. Aleem showed off his swag to his Mother who was standing next to mine. I fished for my money in the pocket where it was supposed to be but it wasn't there. Frantically, or as frantically a little boy could, I looked in my other pockets. My money wasn't there! I could see Mummy's anger rising. She asked gruffly, her tone bordering on shouting, "Where did you put it?"

Well, I didn't know. It was in my pocket a few minutes prior. I knew I took out some to pay for the snacks and of course to re-admire my stash, but then I had replaced the wad back into its rightful pocket. "I am sure of that," I said.

Her exasperation heightened. She screamed, "Then where is it?" The irresponsibility I just displayed was more hurtful to her than the actual loss of money. In that instant, I knew I that she felt that she would be taxed through life for many of my foibles still to come; her little son, was an absent minded, big-eared buffoon and prone to mishap.

Mummy's usually soft loving eyes, now hard as marbles, skewered me in anger. I laid on her a line that was to be a family classic and retold over and over whenever I needed to reminded that I was a moron. I said, "It flew away, like a bird."

Dissapointing Mummy

One of the biggest disappointments I ever foisted on Mummy was at the single performance of our primary school play. It wasn't that I did a poor job. In fact I was probably the star of the show. What I didn't do was tell her *when* we would be on-stage. I didn't want her to attend for I thought she would embarrass me. (Yes, embarrass *me!*). Because of my own childish insecurity, I believed she wasn't as pretty and cool as some of the other Mums who would be in the audience. Like, for example, Hassan Karsanji's mum in her silk finery and lavish jewels. My Mum, I thought, had no pizzazz. I knew she would be dressed in one of her dowdy frocks and would look like a poor relative from a rural Indian village. I couldn't have her mingling with the other parents who would put my own Mummy to shame. After all it was my special day. I had worked so hard for this day and I wanted it to be perfect.

My role in the school play was "Town Crier," and I began the play to announce important news to the cast (and the audience). After ringing a tiny bell, I shouted at the top of my voice that "A magician will appear in our town to decide if we were worthy enough to be awarded with a visit by the King." Only if we displayed tenderness, a sense of true community and good spirits, would the King eventually grace our humble town with a visit.

It was a full-scale play, directed by a prim Englishwoman with a theatrical bent, replete with fancy medieval costumes and a specially constructed set. We were so well rehearsed, that we even thought we could stage a run at the "National Theater" adjacent to the University of Nairobi. Other cast members included cousin Aleem, who appeared as the Mayor, Shelnin Pisani as the Mayor's wife, Hassan Karsanji as the town tailor, and chunky Zaher Bhanji as the friendly, puffy-cheeked baker. The cast had been selected after a school-wide open audition, stamping us as the most talented of kids in the school. It was an honor to be selected and I was thrilled.

Aleem, as the Mayor, also had a fairly large part and we spent many earnest hours rehearsing together and fully memorizing the entire script. Ms. Monica, the button-nosed Englishwoman hired by the school to direct our performance, had stressed that this play would be of the highest possible caliber that we would have to rehearse until we were deemed flawless. We borrowed capes, tights and other items from our parent's friends to lend sizzle to our extraordinary costumes. Hassan even stuck a fake moustache and a tape measure around his neck to look his part as garment-maker to his Excellency the Mayor.

I had the most lines of anyone in the play, and my loud voice easily echoed from the back of the Pavilion Hall where it was being staged. We performed with exuberance, passion and were error free, and when the curtain came down we got thunderous applause and a standing ovation. It was a proud moment for me and, standing there feeling like a Broadway star, I now wished Mummy had been there to see it.

We actors briefly went outside to mingle and bask in our victory with the audience. It also was the last day of school and I was headed off to Mombasa and Grandma Fatu's the very next day. I knew our special time together had come to an end. I saw off each cast member as, one by one, their proud parents came to retrieve them and smother them with adoration. Pops was playing a tennis match somewhere and so he couldn't attend even if I had wanted him to. But not telling Mummy about the venue and time of the performance left me feeling silly, mean and selfish. No one else knew that I hadn't told my mother about the play, but *I* knew. I also realized at that moment that I was a small-minded little twerp who had committed an act of treachery to the one person who meant everything to me.

I turned around and headed back to the stage for one last longing look, when I saw Mummy's smiling face. She said, "I wouldn't have missed your play for anything, my little chokra (boy)." I discovered there and then, that Mothers are better, kinder and more forgiving than anyone's God.

Mummy was a Goddess, but sometimes she was also a bit of a human, rendering an occasional mistake to remind us of her fallibility. A particular error she made was to take me to River Road to get some used ball bearings. For years older kids in the flats built home-made soap-box carts to make use of a relatively steep but short-hill on which races were run. These weren't "soap-box" carts in the true sense since we didn't get soap in wooden boxes, but one gets the picture. Our carts were simple, four ball bearings serving as wheels affixed to a flat wooden chassis. Directional control was obtained by pulling on a sisal string that allowed a small turn of the front axle. It was almost a rite of passage for every boy to build his own "go-cart" and then race for the mythical championship on the hill. We developed an elaborate scheme for measuring our relative success. In short, this depended both on the stability and speed of the vehicle. Relying on pace alone, by choosing a lightweight design, wouldn't furnish a win because the cart had to last through multiple races.

It was also a matter of honor that one used discarded parts and pieces of wood to make the cart. There was no pride in, for example, going to a toy store and getting one that was factory made. No, one had to demonstrate multiple skills to be a winner; be a great driver and cart designer, and a craftsman.

My overzealous pea brain told me that I could easily come up with a killer design and that I was also destined to fare well on the Formula I circuit when I turned 21. The remaining obstacle I faced was how to build the darned thing. I was never good with tools, especially the big hammers, nails and saws which required strength, patience and precision to get something made right. But I was an optimist. I'd figure out how to complete building a cart once I got the most important of components – those valuable ball bearings that would serve as wheels. I don't know if we were fed a lie, but we were led to believe by the older kids that one could obtain the bearings for free at most car repair shops.

So one afternoon I dragged Mummy, to take me on a tour of greasy car repair places where we asked the folks in grimy overalls if we could get used bearings – for free. After our unsuccessful third visit in our suburb of Parklands, Mummy saw the anguish in my face and had a better idea. We drove off to River Road, where, at the bottom of the steep hill down from the Supreme Vegetarian restaurant, were several machine shops. With her kind, open demeanor she soon chatted up an elderly Sikh machinist, who came up with two bearings. But Singh San said he would have to charge nominally for them. I protested and said most people got them free. Mummy ignored my protestations. She had tired of inhaling metal shavings at these grease hovels and promptly paid the man. This put paid to my plan of building something at no cost. It was *such* an embarrassment, and if any of my friends found out, I'd be laughed at for paying for my bearings. But then two bearings were better than none. I needed a set of four, and I told Mummy we could find others elsewhere.

Mummy asked if I was sure; there were other machine shops in the area. I was adamant. I had to show my mates that I could at least get some of my items for free. So we went home with two bearings after I convinced Mummy that I would find the other required pair myself, and I would get them free. Mummy made the mistake of believing me. For the next week, I tried other shops trying to score a pair for free, but I was unsuccessful.

Finally, I gave up on the idea of building my own kart, and rather than blame my stupidity, I pointed the finger at Mummy for poisoning my grand plan. I said we should have tried harder to get the bearings at no cost. Mummy was puzzled and deeply hurt. She had spent an entire afternoon foraging in sweaty shops for her child and she didn't even get a mere "thank you." Instead all she got was a rebuke for ruining my chances at becoming an expert craftsman. It was one of the crueler things I ever did to Mum. But Mummy let the insult slide and soon we were on good terms again. Looking back, I should have been trussed up like a turkey and boiled in motor oil for being an ungrateful, hurtful wretch. I am still haunted by this. So Mums, if you are reading this up there in heaven-land, I want to tell you how very sorry I am.

I have made previous mention of my mother dying from injuries from our horrific car crash. What I have opted not to tell till now is the death wish I had placed on her a few weeks prior. I arrived home very late from witnessing the start of the Safari Rally, and had been AWOL for several hours. This was atypical behavior for me. But then I was in the second year of high school, my voice was cracking, and I was developing whiskers in strange places. I wasn't a little kid anymore, and so I thought I could leave my Mum hanging by disappearing without any notice for almost a full day.

Anyway, I haven't seen Mummy as angry at me and she let me know it, her teeth gritting and issuing me a hardened rebuke worthy of Queen Victoria. Unbalanced by excessive hormones, my seeding oats were shooting up searching for male maturity. I shouted back at her, letting her know that I was older, could do what I wanted, and that she didn't control my life.

Wow! That was a first! I can't ever recall ever raising my voice in anger to her before, and of course it didn't go over too well. Well, who cared? I wasn't her little boy anymore, I was in the second year of high school and I had had a great time witnessing the start of Kenya's most important sporting event. I rubbed it in when I told her I also walked several dangerous miles half way to the airport to see the cars whiz by.

She was shocked and I received more tongue lashing and a look that registered deep disappointment. Well in my own head I knew I didn't care. She could lump it.

For us kids, old and young, The Safari Rally, a 3,000 mile road rally for expert car drivers, was the annual sporting event to follow. *The Daily Nation* and *The East African Standard* devoted hundred of columns of ink to this race considered by many to be the world's toughest. The start of the race was always full of expectation; each kid had a favorite rally driver we could follow during the four day race. We eagerly listened to hourly updates on how our drivers were faring. The rally was a timed course with hundreds of segments. Failure to complete a segment in the allotted time resulted in penalty points. The winner was the one who finished the race with the fewest penalty points. It was all very complicated and so very male, so how dare Mummy encroach on this sacrosanct ground? This wasn't a childish sack race I had gone to see; it was the darned Safari Rally. So what if I was a few hours late?

I looked back at Mummy with an equally stony look and under my breath said, "I just wish you would die. I don't need your silly protection; I have grown into a man." Well Mummy must have heard this and took it to heart, for a few weeks later her Green VW Beetle was smashed to smithereens by a drunken country bus driver. Mummy spent a couple of weeks in hospital before she decided to teach me a final lesson by dying on me. I never told anyone in my family that I, the anointed one, the all powerful spoiled little son, the one who could never do without his Mummy, had disappointed her to death.

Girls Girls Girls

As soon as my hormones kicked in, I thought of girls (sex, really) every three seconds. Yet I also wanted to fall in love with a pretty girl and live happily ever after. Since I had no shot at getting real sex with a real woman, I pleasured myself incessantly. Like Philip Roth's protagonist in *Portnoy's Complaint*, I was much more than addicted. The details of my thirteen-year-old fantasies border on the horrid, so enough said on this topic. But on loving girls, I could fill books with my let-downs and tiny triumphs.

The first girl I considered to be my girlfriend was Narmin Bhaloo, three years my junior. I was 17 when my sister Ferry introduced us at mosque one day and I fell abruptly in love. But getting her to be my girl took an effort. For weeks, I waited outside after Friday mosque hoping to catch another glimpse and a possible run-in. I knew all it would take to win Narmin was to have her reflect my stare; my eyes would be lasers conveying a deep desire. But I never saw her acknowledging my presence on all those evenings I stood resolutely outside the women's exit.

But then as all girls are prone do, Narmin completely surprised me a few weeks into our courtship by sneaking up on me and tapping me on the back. She asked how I was. Tongue-tied, I grunted, and she scampered off laughing with her friend. It was a huge mistake that I knew I had to rectify. The next Friday I summoned all my courage, cornered her and asked how *she* was. She said she was fine. I replied, "Good" and she walked off, her cackling friend in tow. I was ecstatic, another mountain climbed, I told Ferry.

As my guide to romance, Ferry would have none of it. She said I was lazy or scared and that I should have done much better. As my older sister, who understood the strange ways of girls, she said I should quickly move to the next step. That I should ask her out to coffee else she would lose interest. "Too many fish in the sea," Ferry said.

So the next week, I spotted Narmin, strode confidently up to her, and in front of her rude, giggly friend asked her if she wanted to have coffee with me at the Hilton on Saturday morning. (Anyone who was anyone and who had a girl went to display his prize at the Hilton). In a monotone Narmin said, "Maybe" and walked off. What kind of an answer was maybe? Ferry comforted me and said it was an emphatic yes, and that I should go meet her at her father's store that sold stereo equipment.

I agonized over what to wear, but then settled on a pair of silver bell-bottoms and a pink shirt. As soon as I peered into her father's shop, Narmin strode out confidently and said we were to go to the Nairobi Aquarium across the street.

"Don't you want a coffee at the Hilton?" I asked, foolishly trying to seal the deal.

Narmin would have none of it. "I'm not your girlfriend" she rebuked. So I followed her meekly.

I paid the few shillings for our entrance. She walked briskly around the various glass boxes, making note of the colorful fish, as I tried to follow and make conversation. At the Aquarium's café, Narmin stopped abruptly. She then said the sweetest words I ever heard, "Buy me a coffee," she demanded. She gulped it down in a flash, said goodbye and left me there feeling like a conqueror.

The next Friday I asked if she wanted to listen to some new music I had on cassette. I had driven Pops' Alfa Romeo to the mosque in high anticipation. I believed that if I lured her into the car I could kiss her. She told me to drive off as she lowered her head. She didn't want to be seen leaving with me. I didn't mind, she had after all agreed to come with me, in my car. This qualified as a genuine girlfriend-boyfriend inter-action. I drove down the bottom of a steep dark hill a few minutes away from the mosque. Except for crickets chirping it was deathly quiet and frighteningly romantic. I reached over. She opened her mouth wide as if to get her teeth cleaned. Our tongues met. It felt strange and gross, but it was my first kiss.

My relationship with Narmin ended abruptly the following week. I had put on a flashy suit and one again I lurked in the shadows waiting for her to emerge from the mosque when Aleem pointed her out to me. She was standing with that dreaded Shiraz Premji, clinging to his every word and laughing with him. I approached her thinking I could wrest her away from my opponent. She was rightfully mine; after all I had kissed her. Instead all Narmin said was, "Leave me alone." When a woman means no, she really means no. I skulked away.

Undeterred by this fiasco I searched for new love and hope. My good friend Adil was dating Anis, a pert, cute thing at Pangani mosque and said he knew of a suitable candidate. But with a 15 minute drive from Parklands, this was a distance and a commitment. Adil said insisted I should go with him to meet Anis's cousin, Shemin. He said Shemin was a stunning beauty. With nothing to lose, pride to recover, and a love to gain, I went off with Adil to Pangani mosque. The girls came into the open verandah outside the main building. Here females could mix briefly with males without appearing as sluts. Adil motioned, and we went to greet Anis. Standing next to her was Shemin, a doe-eyed beauty with clear skin and a lovely body. I fell in love and then we were intro-duced. Shemin told me she lived in Ngara, I replied that I lived in the

Highridge area of Parklands. Adil arranged to meet Anis on Saturday in Town, and I finally had my introduction.

I knew I had to strike immediately, for fish like Shemin are like very large tuna, rare to find and almost priceless. This urge to love made me brave. I borrowed Pops' car and drove to her house the very next day. Shemin's' mother opened the door. In a most mature effort, I asked her if Shemin was home.

Shemin came down the stairs in a ragged and very modest night-dress. She was stunned to see me, as she should have been. I hadn't told her I was coming to her house to freak out her mother. Instead I lied and said I was in the "area" visiting my friend Ladka who lived close by. Shemin said, "Good" and fell silent. I stood there foolishly, with Shemin's mother looking on suspiciously. Not knowing what else to say, I, too, said goodbye and made my exit. But I was elated; it was another completed battle in my long conquest for seeking love.

The next few Fridays, I went with Adil to Pangani mosque. But I had to ogle Shemin from afar. Shemin was ultra conservative, shy and religious and thought I'd simply get frustrated and leave. But my pursuit was on. At my prodding Adil managed to get his girl Anis to bring Shemin to the movies. I would then just happen to "run into them" at the box office.

Shemin clearly saw through the façade, and appeared perturbed. But she went along and sat next to me. At first, she took pains to make sure that we didn't have any kind of physical contact. Eventually she relaxed enough and I managed to position my cotton shirt to graze her cardigan once. I repeated the move and she didn't flinch. This, I thought, was enough great progress for a single day and I shifted in my seat to avoid any more contact.

After the movie, I suggested we have a snack at a nearby café. Shemin had terror in her eyes. She was vehemently against any more socializing. At that point I knew that I had to use all the weasel craft at my disposal to win her over. I decided on the classic male frontal attack, I asked her, "Are you scared of going?"

She protested meekly, "Of course not".

So I asked, somehow mustering great confidence, "So what's the problem?" Shemin had no answer and so with only minor urging from Anis we went to the Exotica.

It became easier to do these dates after that. Shemin was intrigued by the odor of male, took a liking to me, or needed to cover for her cousins' Anis's torrid love affair with Adil. (I knew it was the latter but I didn't mind). My love, my raison d'être was sitting next to me

The four of us roamed around Nairobi, in Adil's mothers green Honda civic; Adil and Anis in front, smitten and holding hands. We would take trips to remote locations such as the Casino in Thika (20 miles away), or the Utalii hotel in Muthaiga. But through all this Shemin was almost as mute as a doorstop; she would look out of her window for long stretches, avoiding eye contact, as if the yearning in my eyes would blind her. The drives were pretty, but not *that* pretty.

When she finally said something, these rare utterances were usually banal or depressing. "Those pineapples look prickly?" Or, "What time do you think we will get home?" I took solace in that she had a voice and she was saying something; if not directly to me, then to all the occupants in the car, of which I was one. I took this as a clear sign to carry on with my pursuit. I would eventually break her down.

After several such "dates" we found ourselves sitting on the Utalii's hotel's rolling lawn with a view of the pretty Muthaiga valley below. Adil and Anis had gone for a lovers' stroll. I knew it was now or never. With the courage of all men channeled into my heart, I placed my hand on her open palm. We sat looking at yellow wild-flowers strewn all over the lush green. She let my hand rest there, and I knew she could be mine.

Holdings hands is not fully committal, especially if the other party doesn't counter with a reassuring a squeeze. I had to go the next step. What I wanted I wanted was a kiss to cement our relationship. I leaned over to kiss her, and she was horrified. "What are you doing?" she squawked.

"I think you are beautiful. I wanted to kiss you."

"Not now" she said embarrassed, giggling as if I had let out a fart. But I took that as a victory; a kiss was in the offing and our fate would be sealed.

We went on several more foursomes; the silent pair at the back, the jabbering lovebirds in front. I mentioned to Shemin that I wrote an account of every date I had with her. The notion of her "dates" being recorded for posterity horrified her. She said flatly, "Don't write about me!"

I said, "How could I not? You are precious, like an oxygen tank under water, and it's my diary, no one else will see it."

Shemin's smooth lips went into a pout. She pleaded, "Please don't write about me. What if you lose your diary and someone finds out. I'd get into so much trouble and so would Anis."

I had an answer for that. "But that's why I never spell your full name. In my journal you are simply known as 'S' not Shemin."

"It doesn't matter," Shemin complained. "Everyone knows what Anis and Adil do."

"What they do? What do you mean?" I lied. I knew Adil and Anis went farther than first base on his parents' bed.

Shemin said, "Well they shouldn't be doing heavy kissing. It's dangerous."

A gleam of hope shot through my chest. "Heavy kissing?" I questioned with fake disbelief. "I would never do heavy kissing," but then ramming through the opening, I asked "What about a light kiss?"

Shemin giggled, and closed her eyes. Our lips met, ever so softly; our tongues not touching. Her eyes opened. My task accomplished, she rubbed off the slick on her lips with the back of her hand.

Sadiq Uncle

If there was ever a man with a kooky sense of humor, an odd ball, and a heart of gold, it was Sadiq Uncle, father to my cousins Aleem and Aisha, and husband of lovely Sultan Aunty. There so many little stories in my head that I could possibly fill up a book and still not exhaust the wondrous, whimsical nature of this kind man.

For starters he called me "Pocha Singh" ever since I could recognize his face that sported a pair of eyes that darted about incongruently and creepily. It is a queer thing to ascribe the term "Singh" to a skinny runt like me. Sikhs are warriors, are strong, have integrity and backbone, all of which I had none when growing up, and have cultivated little of to date. The term "Pocha" or "Soft" in Gujarati, however, fits me perfectly. I crater under pressure, hate crusty foods, and still prefer bread soaked in milk to a crunchy carrot any day. So giving me the nickname of "Pocha Singh" was a powerful oxymoron. I took solace in that at least he called me "Soft Singh," instead of something cruel like "Slimy Shrimp."

Sadiq Uncle was an accountant and worked for Twentsche Overseas Trading Company which had, among other functions, wholesaler distribution rights for all Philips Electronics products sold in East Africa. One evening Sadiq Uncle came in carrying a big brown box in his arms. He promptly set it on the floor, opened up the package and placed a shiny new Phillips TV smack-dab onto our low-slung mahogany coffee table. Sadiq Uncle had just brought to our home what is by far my favorite trapping of modern society – the television.

We were only the second family own in our compound of 93 families to get a TV –Sadiq Uncle got the first set for his family – and so this catapulted us into the most fashionable of families. It was a bit after my fourth birthday and the "Voice of Kenya" had begun test broadcasting of black and white television on its single channel. I loved everything about the TV, even the test pattern which preceded the beginning of the daily broadcast. The test pictures, which looked like something out of an episode of *Dr. Who* or *The Twilight Zone*, sent me into a trance. I suppose if the Kenyan Government wanted to forever mesmerize me with media why not try and be full-bore hypnotic?

I was popular for a brief period as some older boys begged Pops to let them catch a glimpse of the magic displayed on the curved screen. This sudden popularity waned quickly as TVs sprang up in the flats like psychedelic mushrooms growing on cow manure on a wet, cool night. (Yes, magic 'shrooms do grow on cow manure. Please don't inquire how I know. I just do). The TV was made using 1960's technology of course, which meant there were a bunch of vacuum tubes functioning as the main circuitry. I remember looking through the air vents at the glowing red of the tubes in the back, amazed at how mere glass ampoules could turn into pictures on the screen.

Perry Mason was my mother's favorite show. Pops and Mum liked the intellectual challenge of guessing the murderer and her motive. While it came on late I was allowed to watch as I as I nestled to sleep on Mummy's lap. I loved watching my parents made happy by this piece of magic furniture, and still am grateful to Sadiq Uncle for having provided us with our first TV set. Pops sure was less surly when the TV was on.

Sadiq Uncle loved contraptions and fixing things. He often carried with him a toolbox, and went around relatives houses fixing electric sockets, broken valves, dripping taps and the like. Mummy said he liked giving back and was very generous but I thought he wanted to avoid Sultan Aunty. Like her twin Shirin, Sultan Aunty was a non-stop, world-class chatterbox. She went on and on like a spastic bird muttering to herself, to plants and trees and to inanimate objects and flying insects. So when Sadiq Uncle brought home a noisy African Grey parrot, I thought it was a lovely gesture of love. The parrot, who lived in a circular cage, became Sultan Aunty's constant companion, and together they exchanged recipes and great conversations on the meaning of life. I also thought it kept Sultan Aunty from going crazy. The parrot – conveniently named Kasuku or "parrot" in Swahili – figured out how to mimic Sultan Aunty perfectly. The uninitiated visiting her house often thought she was exchanging nonsensical volleys with her visiting sister Shirin.

Sadiq Uncle was born on the tiny island of Mafia at the southern end of the Tanzanian coast. Mummy told me it was as remote a place as one could find; perhaps this was why Sadiq Uncle didn't have much to say. I always thought that was a reasonable explanation. I had a romantic notion of him spending much of his childhood looking out to the sparkling Indian Ocean, fishing for food when he needed it, and playing Crusoe to a kind, smiling African Friday. But Sadiq Uncle was never much for stories, so I never found out many details of his childhood or how his parents ended up in such a remote place. But one thing he brought with him to landlocked, mountainous Nairobi from Mafia was his incredible passion for fish. He bought only the freshest of fish, and he would get his at the fish branch of the Reata Road Market. Each day a truck owned by Reata would make a trip from the Mombasa on the coast bringing its bounty of snapper, wahoo, prawns, spiny lobster, sand shark and whatever else the local fishermen could catch in their shallow boats.

As was his style Sadiq couldn't buy just one type of fish, he fell in love with several varieties, and so Sultan Aunty who did the cooking, experimented with all shapes and sizes of fish. I hated most fish from the fear of pointy bones puncturing my throat. Often, however, Sadiq Uncle would bring home fresh fillets we called "Kingfish" which had only a few easy-to-spot bones. I ended loving this kind of fish when cooked in a rich tomato-based masala. Over the years, in my efforts to impress girls with my pretentious knowledge of what uppity English folks ate, I also made it to trying Dover sole and rainbow trout.

One day Sultan Aunty labored over a strange looking, puffy, colored fish that Sadiq Uncle had brought home. It was many years later in Tokyo's Tsukiji Fish market that I made a hyper-imaginative connection. I realized there, among the vast mounds of tuna, octopi and stern looking Japanese with sharp knives, that the fish Sadiq Uncle brought home that day must have been the poisonous variety of blowfish. If not prepared correctly, blowfish can send the diner into a paroxysm and certain death. As I mulled over this I was sure Sadiq Uncle as a man of the sea must have known about this oddity. Who, then, was Sadiq Uncle trying to kill?

Clearly it wasn't me Sadiq Uncle was targeting but most likely my uncle Badru (Pops and Sultan Aunty's older brother). Badru Uncle was a royal pain to everyone who passed his way and made lewd jokes that always fell flat. His behavior irritated the normally placid and warm Sadiq Uncle.

Well, Badru Uncle was invited for lunch that day when the "blowfish" was served. I recall that he made a big deal about its exquisite taste with his normal and unwarranted bombast. I remember Sadiq Uncle looking on expectantly to see if Badru Uncle would collapse into a doddering heap. Well fortunately for those of us who were fond of Sadiq Uncle, Badru Uncle didn't collapse, and there was no murder investigation. Perhaps Sultan Aunty had saved her brother by cooking it correctly.

My cousin Aleem (Sadiq Uncle's son) loved his Dad's connection to the ocean and so too became a fastidious experimenter of fruits of the sea. Aleem loved and ate whatever seafood came his way. Well, one afternoon, after stuffing himself full of giant curried prawns, Aleem' face swelled up like a football and his lips gained a strange purplish hue. It turned out he had become allergic to shellfish. (All I can say with perfect envy is that it served Aleem right for being everyone's favorite and the smartest boy in school). To rub it in, I soon began my own long love affair with shrimp and mollusks of any kind.

Sadiq Uncle had other habits which I thought were queer. He never drank a drop of liquor and was desperately embarrassed to see anyone imbibe. If he saw someone inebriated, for example if Pops had a couple of beers in him and was being jolly, Sadiq Uncle would not stay and visit despite Mummy's or my protestations.

Sadiq Uncle also never attended large family gatherings unless they were hosted at his house. Even at his home he'd rather hang out with the squawking parrot in the outside verandah than carry on any type conversation with a male relative. But Sadiq Uncle was an expert at making baby talk with little infant relatives. He loved kids and the kids loved him back, and they had a special language of their own that worked. I'm convinced that any kid who has been adored by Sadiq Uncle is cooler than one who hasn't. With his wild success as child leader I learned that it is better to spend time talking to young, earnest children than to adults who are full of themselves.

As a man of habit, Sadiq Uncle attended mosque daily but would insist on driving 15 minutes to the central mosque in city centre rather than pray at the one much closer to home in Parklands. After prayers, he volunteered for extra work at the mosque. When he arrived home, Sultan Aunty would his have his meal waiting which he would swallow faster than Usain Bolt. Then he would drink a cup of instant coffee and go to bed, the caffeine, oddly enough, needed for a restful sleep; the coffee did this every night I saw him when hanging out with my buddy Aleem.

The only time he changed his routine was on Friday. After Friday evening services in the central mosque, he would drive home to have his meal. He would then drive *back* to the city to see a first run Indian movie at the Embassy, Shan or Globe cinema. While there, he would promptly go to sleep before the scene when the hero or heroine got into trouble. (For lovers of Indian movies, this means well before the second love song). He said repeatedly, and I thought only half-jokingly to anyone within earshot, "With a wife like mine, I need to go to the movies for some peace and quiet."

Giving back to the community and his family was Sadiq Uncle's way of living a useful life. He is alive today and still is a funny odd man. But he is also a shining beacon of how man's generosity can alter the minds of little boys.

Papa and Tennis

I may have already mentioned that Papa was somewhat of a Kenyan tennis demigod. When I hit middle age, Pops and I were on excellent terms. We now shared everything from silly jokes to single malts. Over our fourth cold beer before noon on a Saturday morning, Pops told me that he played tennis only to keep himself from becoming a lush and drug addict. The discipline to become a good tennis player involved a daily work-out and an hour of practice. Without tennis, he said, he would have drunk his way through life while sampling all kinds of mind-altering substances. (How tragic!).

When twenty, Pops' early morning routine involved 45 minutes of running, skipping rope or calisthenics followed by an hour of solid hitting. In the evening after finishing work, he would catch the bus home, change into his tennis outfit and head to the courts.

This perseverance and discipline paid off. He became an expert player and that got him into all the private British clubs and their white members who wanted to challenge this upstart darkie. There were several private clubs in Kenya, where if you weren't white enough or a great player, you could simply not get in. They included among others, Karen Country Club, Nairobi Club, and Parklands.

The Nairobi Club was the most royal of these clubs. It was where they held the Kenya Open Championship each year. Center court was fashioned after its cousin in Wimbledon except that instead of grass, the surface was deep, red clay. One year Pops and his partner Aziz Meghji reached the Open Championship doubles final and insisted on taking Ferry and me to watch. It was the year of Rozy's birth and Pops said that was a good omen. He had been striving for years to make it to the Kenya Open final. When he finally did, he wanted family to bear witness. Mummy would never go to his matches. She was far too shy and modest and I think Pops liked it that way. So Ferry and I went instead. We were nervous with anticipation and were ready half an hour early.

It was my first time to see the pomp and etiquette of a white country club. Mummy told us to behave and be extremely polite. Ferry had on a pretty dress and Mummy tried to improve on my usual frumpy untidiness. Since we arrived early, Pops took us on a little tour of the place. It was sprawling with tons of well-groomed tennis courts including the stadium-like Center Court. Next to the topiary-gated club entrance was a cricket pitch with actual turf (not lowly matting) to bat from. It also had a billiard table like green for lawn bowling. Ferry and I looked on in semi-amazement as old fogies in lily-white outfits rolled what looked like small cannon balls and pretended it was difficult. And right behind the center court was an imposing clubhouse with a cavernous dining room, a sparkling chandelier as its centerpiece.

Even at that early age, I noted that such clubs were where married men stashed and met their "girlfriends," boozed excessively and dined on "mixed grills" served by docile uniformed African waiters. I absorbed all of this pretentious panache, storing it into my impressionable eight-year-old brain. It was a keen glimpse of the lives of the privileged in colonial Kenya. As brown children, I knew we could never crack that barrier, because we would never be white. But it helped to know how the exalted lived. It was, we felt, a high privilege walking the vast hallowed grounds where the Queen once may have had lunch. For years after 1 used my visit to Nairobi Club as a template from which to copy the eccentric ways of the British.

Ferry and I sat in one of the first rows and watched five scintillating sets of tennis. Finally, match point arrived, and I heard the voice of the umpire shout: "Game, set and match to Nanji and Meghji." Pops had won! It was perhaps the proudest moment of his life and also my own. The large silver cup, with names of past champions tastefully engraved at the base, bespoke glory. I hugged the trophy. I could forever boast that my very own dad was a champion, and by birthright, I, too, would inherit this status.

I begged Papa to take us to more matches, and he kindly did. Pops won many tournaments and was a finalist at many others. Our "sitting room" was adorned with trophies of all sizes and it was a constant reminder for me to excel and be disciplined. I guess I didn't like being reminded, for unlike Pops, I never mastered any single sport.

Pops had a membership at the Aga Khan Club, but because of his tennis skills was also nominated to join the mostly white Parklands club. While it wasn't regal and vast like Nairobi Club, Parklands was well maintained and was a pretty place. It also had a swimming pool, and on Sundays the club served a poolside brunch. It was there where I first saw and tried a plateful of gorgeous-looking purple beets. The taste and texture of the beets did not match with their visual appeal, and I have never eaten a beet since.

We went swimming a few times in the nice pool; or rather I waded and splashed about like a spastic ostrich while Ferry swam laps. One hot Sunday we begged Pops to take us swimming. He obliged and dropped us off as went to play a couple of sets of tennis. Ferry was already in the pool while I was outside pulling out the lint from my belly button, when I heard two white British girls about my age sniggering and pointing in my direction. I thought they were commenting at something behind me and I ignored them. They jumped into the pool and Ferry came out for a breather. I thought I would meet these two beauties one of whom who spoke loud enough for me to hear in a shrilly English accent, "Oh look! The clean water has become a dirty, dirty brown. Let's leave, Patty".

It was one of the crueler things anyone has ever said to me. I never went back to swim at Parklands Club. I didn't want the abuse. But I did go to watch an amazing, courageous club tennis final the year Pops won the Kenya Championship. He was on a tear and had been unbeatable with his partner Aziz Meghji. As a Papa looked up to smash a lob up. His partner Aziz shouted, "Mine, mine" a bit too late. Aziz's racket came down hard on Papa's face shattering his spectacles. Shards of glass went into Papa's eye. The match was halted, and an attendant with some kind of medical experience washed out his eye with water. I actually saw a couple of glass pieces removed. Pops could have defaulted at that point but this was the final and wanted to continue. He asked me to run quickly to our car, where in the glove compartment, he stored his prescription sunglasses. It was the fastest I have ever run.

Papa put on the dark glasses, but it was about 5 PM in Nairobi. Sunlight was disappearing fast, and long evening shadows cluttered the court further impairing his vision. Yet, the injury gave Papa and Meghji added momentum, and they soon closed out the match winning the final set with ease. Pops carried home yet another large trophy, and I was bursting with pride from both Pops and my heroism. (I had run quite fast to the car, hadn't I?). The next day Pops went to see Dr Sandhu, the Sikh eye specialist to make sure that his eye was OK. Dr. Sandhu examined him, washed his eye out with some solution and pulled another sliver of glass that had lodged firmly under his eyelid. When I found this out, I was thrilled not for Papa's eye, but for me. I now had an even cooler story to tell my friends.

At the Aga Khan club, Papa would play tennis with a set of Indian hackers who were nowhere close to him in talent. Yet, Pops liked playing on his "home" court. There was great camaraderie among his group of interesting characters who cracked lewd jokes that I enjoyed. Kamaludin, one of the younger unmarried guys, never took off his dark glasses because he thought that would impress women. He had them on matter how dark it became. Even when striking a cue ball in the snooker room's dim light, Kamaludin would wear his shades. I didn't know how he could tell the blue ball from the black and frankly he looked silly shooting balls like some blind person. But I wasn't going to tell him that; he was an elder twice my size and his raging temper on the tennis court was as bad as McEnroe's. He always lost to Pops in tennis which infuriated him. The last thing he would want from Pops' pipsqueak of a son would be to tell him his snooker would improve if he took a brighter view of life.

Badru "Googlo" was another of Pops' friends. He had an annoying lisp but made up for this by bearing an awesome looking daughter called Kuku (Chicken). I asked Pops from how his odd nickname of "Googlo" came about. Pops had no answer. But through my intrepid detective skills, I found out that it was a name Badru adopted for himself. To overcome the drawback of his lisp he falsely spread the word that he was a gigolo. Well, boys being boys in the 1940s, they changed that to Googlo, a name that decades later was possibly inventively stolen by a bunch of guys from Stanford needing a cool name for the "search engine" they were developing.

I had obtained my secret information from Malik Dhalla another of Papa's tennis buddies. Malik Dhalla was an informer's informant. It seemed he knew everything about everybody in our community. Any dirt on anyone could be exhumed by Malik Dhalla. He was marvelous at trading information which also led to an amazing array of valuable connections.

Need hard to obtain "movie" tickets for a sold out show? No problem, Malik Dhalla was your man. Need to know where you could cheap air-tickets to the U.K.? Dhalla was your man. Need an almost impossible to a obtain telephone line at home? No worries, Dhalla could shorten the wait time by years. Dhalla was also Sadiq Uncle's good friend and daily they rode together to the city and mosque. Both were devout teetotalers and supreme fix-it guys. Having both of them in our family orbit,

I thought, was a direct reflection of Mummy's character, who both men adored for her purity and humility.

Even though he was a sorry excuse of a tennis player, Pops enjoyed having Dhalla around for his rich tapestry of stories, deep reservoir of off-color jokes and loyalty. They were very good friends, this odd pair; one a master tennis player partial to whisky, and the other a tennis hack who didn't drink. On Sunday after early morning mosque services, they would often go for a drive and talk about horse racing, the ample bosoms of some Indian actresses and the impeccable shot-making of Rod Laver. If I could get up in the wee hours of the morning, Pops would take me along with him. These were cherished moments for me. If we were early enough, we could catch a beautiful African sunrise over the vast open fields of Embakasi Airport and Nairobi National park. After having seen the immensity of nature's beauty we would then head off to the Supreme Hotel for an early breakfast of puris, jalebis, and masala tea.

A vice Malik Dhalla could not shake was his love for betting on horse racing. The races were run in the U.K. and were not televised in Nairobi. To win anything Dhalla had to rely on the written words or form sheets supplied by of a bunch of English cockneys on Fleet Street. He told Pops that a major goal of life was to complete the ever elusive "trifecta ". With this deep passion for studiously poring over form sheets, Pops was convinced of Dhalla's capabilities to accurately gauge a horse's chances of winning from a distance of a mere 5,000 miles. So mostly for amusement and anticipation, Pops, put down ten shillings every week, and let Dhalla bet on what he thought was right. Malik would make his choices on Saturday mornings at the "Brighton Turf Accountants" – legal bookies in Nairobi. We would wait the results of any wins on the Sunday morning trips. A couple of times Pops won some money, making the sunrises over the airport that much sweeter.

The legal bookies were also where one could play the "football pools" or gamble on the English and Scottish football leagues. The goal was to pick eight draws from the 80 or so matches held every week; one point was awarded if your selections ended in a home win, two points for an away win, and three points for a draw. The magic number of 24 points or eight draws resulted in a hefty payout, with winnings dropping precipitously for reaching lower points. With my religious-like following of Arsenal FC and the English leagues I thought I had an inbuilt advantage handicapping results. So I persuaded Pops to let me try wagering on the pools. Pops humored me and forked over some cash to Malik Dhalla who submitted my filled-in sheets. I never hit 24 points, although once I managed to come close with 21 points, but did not win anything. Pops eventually put a stop to my budding gambling career after realizing he was throwing good money after bad.

I thought this sudden arrest was unfair and to prove my expertise I entered "mock" pools. To prevent cheating, I handed my picks to Aleem on Saturday afternoon. As Saturday evening arrived, we would sit listening to match results on the BBC using Sadiq Uncle's powerful shortwave radio. Aleem would then tally the points and let me know if I had that magic 24 or come close to it. Well despite my innate expertise, I never got anything above 21 points and learned that gambling always favored the house.

Misspent Youth

Nairobi's snooker rooms were a male enclave; a place for cigarettes, bawdy talk and camaraderie. At 14 we were too young to play at the Aga Khan club's pristine tables. Musa, the club manager, resolutely refused to let unaccomplished kids ruin his beloved felt. But playing at the club was a goal for many boys. We wanted to spend lazy Saturday and Sunday afternoons among older men who regaled each other with inflated stories of drinking, sex and assorted forms of debauchery.

To play at the club we had to learn. Our only options for an education were Nairobi's public snooker halls – Delite and Sequieras. These were vestiges of gaudy establishments that in colonial times served as "clubs" for Indians. Sequieras was in the basement of a building next to the famous Sombrero striptease club that imported light skinned Egyptian, Turkish and Greek girls. We knew this because we saw their suggestive ads in the *Daily Nation* behind the classifieds and in front of the sports pages. Wearing frilly knickers, boas, and displaying ample but bra-covered breasts they connoted a boy's paradise.

Delite was in a large room on the second floor of the venerable "Green Hotel and Restaurant", a fluorescently-lit haven for boozing, barbecued meat and other roadside snacks. Across the street from the Green Hotel was the Odeon Cinema where you could take your rented-mistress to see a second-run movie. After the credits rolled you might take her for a few tots, a cheap dinner and then spill seed in one of the low cost rooms at the hotel.

It was exactly this kind of grime that attracted us 13 year old boys. No adult who we might recognize would ever rat on us; their own indiscretions would be fiercely probed. Delite's snooker room had three tired old tables, begging for new slate and felt. It cost two shillings to turn on the lights, and a shilling for each additional half hour. The balls were chipped and the cues bent, but it was a place to learn the ways of men.

We snuck out of school early Wednesday afternoons, a time usually set aside for extracurricular activities such as chess, debating, marksmanship or the radio club. In our packs we carried long pants. Damji and Kydo also brought cigarettes and matches, although Karsanji and I were still too naive to enjoy smokes. Besides, I had promised Mummy I would never smoke on account of Papa's own vile habit. So Karsanji and I watched as our friends made smoke rings and grew into maturity. Playing snooker at the Delite or Sequieras was proof enough for reaching the exalted goal of miscreant adult behavior; we didn't also need our lungs feeling like sandpapered wood.

We also thought that once we finished snooker at Sequieras we could sneak into Sombreros to ogle at breasts and other female flesh. We tried this on a couple of occasions, but there was a strict admittance policy of "over 21" and the rejections were embarrassing. Expressing sour grapes, we quickly decided that Delite was better.

After several Wednesday afternoon visits of snooker practice at Delite, we became comfortable with sleaze. We ordered greasy snacks, Damji and Kydo smoked openly like accomplished hoodlums, and we all flirted with the pay-for-hire ladies hovering over the bar. One prostitute even wanted to kidnap Karsanji on account of his good looks and improbable green eyes. She offered him a free "visit upstairs". But at 14 and still a virgin, Karsanji was too chicken to accept.

We eventually became snooker players of some merit or at least we now knew how not to rip felt. The exalted doors of the Aga Khan club's snooker room were now open to us. From then on we spent hundreds of hours trying to improve our play against some very good players. By the time I was 17 I thought I was good enough to put my hat in for the Kenya Open. I lost easily in the first round but I now had a badge that falsely claimed I belonged with the country's best sharpshooters.

Snooker wasn't the only focus for wasting time. I also took a passion to pinball machines. A personal goal was to master every machine by racking up enough points for a free game. My first pinball experience was at age eleven at the "Chicken Inn" next to the large mosque in the City Centre. On significant religious occasions Papa would want to offer Friday prayers at this glittering central mosque rather than the smaller one in Parklands.

As soon as prayers were over, Pops would sneak out for a couple of quick drinks at Sans Chic, one of the bars close by. I took this opportunity to head to Chicken Inn with a bunch of change. Mummy didn't take too kindly to our visits; Pops shouldn't be drinking right after being absolved of sin, and I was scolded for choosing a path of gambling and eventual ruin. I insisted that pinball had nothing to do with gambling; that it was a game of skill and that these were not one-armed bandits. Mummy thought otherwise and disapproved sharply. But with Pops enjoying a couple of beers, I knew I had time to sneak in a game or two.

Before long I had found out which Nairobi bars and restaurants had pinball machines and I soon became a regular at many watering holes. Of course I didn't drink, and didn't want to, but I became addicted to pinball. I assiduously avoided the Highridge Bar close to our flats, for that was Papa's favorite spot to imbibe; everywhere else was open territory. One holiday month I walked several miles each day to take advantage of a faulty machine that offered free games at Park Lodge, a brothel for high-end prostitutes. Another time, I insisted on Papa taking us to eat at a place famous for its barbecued pork. As Muslims we didn't eat pig but the restaurant's staggering hoard of three shiny pinball machines prompted me at least find out what burned pig flesh smelled like. Since this place also served beef and lamb, we were spared the ignominy of not eating while occupying a table. Pops had a beefsteak; Ferry and Rosy each had a glass of ginger ale while I had blast with my three new inanimate friends.

By the time I was 17, Elton's John rendition of "Pinball Wizard" became my anthem, even if I couldn't make out all the lyrics. Ignominiously I didn't know that song's subject was a blind boy. All I had bouncing around in my head were the words "Pinball Wizard" which meant I was fulfilling my destiny.

In my mind's-eye, I was one of the of the world best pinball players. With a fistful of change, any machine was exposed. I would quickly find machines' weaknesses and the nuances that could supply me with easy bonus points. I dreamt of flying around the world to compete in pinball competitions accompanied by a retinue of adoring fans. Lured by fame, I sponsored with co-addict Hanif, an unsanctioned world championship at the Exotica Restaurant. Our entry fee was 20 Shillings with the winner taking all. We had eight people sign up, all regulars of our informal pinball circuit. (We would run into these guys at other city bars and restaurants).

The tourney format was a simple playoff; the winner needing three of the five games per match to progress. My claim for glory was crushed in the very first round. I lost 3-1 to a Sunni Muslim with a hare-lip. But used to losing at everything, I wasn't devastated. In our mosque there was a framed saying by someone exalted, which wisely pointed out, "If at first you fail, you must try and try again. Defeat or victory is in the hands of God but struggle is a man's joy." The exalted one was clearly thinking of me when writing that.

The most embarrassing parts of my misspent youth were my visits to prostitutes. As 17 and 18 year boys with raging hormones, we taunted each other for being virgins. We had to prove our manhood by engaging in the dirty deed. Making it with our Indian girls was out of the question. If caught we would mightily embarrass our families for taking advantage of vulnerable girls. Worse, even if one of our million "boys" got trapped by a fertile egg we would be forced to marry the girl in a shotgun wedding. Even as foolish boys we knew these were high stakes. So, instead, most of us got educated at one of the Arab or African brothels around town. I matriculated from the Lucky Lodge on my 18th birthday with an unsatisfying, short experience. To complete my post-graduate training I sampled a couple of other spots, before deciding it was demeaning to pay for sex. I wanted women to want me.

College Bound

*P*ops loved travelling: the smell of different bars and foods, the throb of large cities like Bombay, New York and the splendid variety of women God has placed on this earth. Papa told us his travels were to "discover the world," and to scope the possibility of a better life outside of our vulnerable Kenyan cocoon.

When I was about 12, Pops went on a discovery mission to the U.S. and Canada. His aim was to find out the peculiar differences that separate America from its neighbor to the north. Pops came back full of stories. Since he had travelled in the early summer he informatively noted that there was no difference between the two countries. The weather, he found out, is hotter in Houston than in Vancouver, but Houston wasn't half as pretty. On the other hand Toronto had nothing on New York. Pops loved Times Square, the Empire State Building and the Statue of Liberty. He even went up for a drink at a restaurant high up in the Twin Towers. "Magnificent. Nothing like it, I tell you," he had said.

But Pops said his favorite place was Berkeley, California. Pops had gone on a campus tour and had witnessed its majesty. Thrilled with seeing the Berkeley Cyclotron that could smash atoms, Pops said I should attend college there.

With this ringing endorsement from Pops, I had no other choice but to let this seed germinate. Infused with the same euphoria by Pops, cousin Aleem also felt that America should be a choice for his higher education. The only worry we had about America was its lascivious dependence on illegal drugs. We didn't want to become bhang (marijuana) addicts like everyone else there. But Aleem and I agreed that as well trained Muslims we had a resolve of steel and would never take alcohol or smoke weed.

To apply to American colleges we would have to take the Scholastic Aptitude Test (SAT). We were dumbfounded when we found that only English and Math were going to be tested. What! No chemistry, biology or world history? This was going to be too easy for a pair of smart 16-year-olds. One Saturday, without trying any practice exams, Aleem and I strode confidently into the United States Educational Institute near the US Embassy and took the SATs. Six weeks later we got an official looking report from the Education Testing Lab in Princeton, New Jersey. My scores ranked me in the 70th percentile of all others who had taken that test. Aleem beat my scores, of course, but his scores weren't close to stellar at the 80th percentile. I was upset, but Aleem suffered a huge blow to his ego.

We vowed to retake the test a year later; we couldn't have the blemish of mediocrity on our academic records. With pre-test practice, we improved substantially. Aleem, of course, did better than I did and ended up in the 99th percentile for both Math and English; I hovered at 97% which meant that only 3% of all those taking the exam did better. Only 3% of the kids in the vast, wide USA were smarter than me! Ha! We now knew were going to America! All we had to do was apply to colleges and universities; someone would accept us!

After a couple of weeks of poring over the *Peterson's College Guide*, a fat volume describing each college campus and possible areas of study, I finalized my list. Using primary criteria of wanting hot American babes and warm weather (I was born in steamy Mombasa), I applied to four warm weather universities and one obligatory Ivy League school. These were the Universities of California at Berkeley, Miami, Texas at Austin, Notre Dame and Cornell. Except for Cornell which was stuck in the snowy drifts near Canada someplace, I knew I had selected well.

Texas, Florida, and California - now those were places *everyone* knew. Florida had Miami Beach and bikinis; Texas had naughty cowgirls and was near the Gulf of Mexico. Beloved California was the home of palm trees, Barnaby Jones and Perry Mason, and cartoons. My gaffe was thinking that South Bend, Indiana, the home of Notre Dame, was warm, dry and dusty. The State of Indiana evoked images of spaghetti westerns and cowboys shooting at Red Indians hiding behind cactuses. And how more far south could one get than South Bend? How was I supposed to know the name and precise location of each state and town in the 50 states that made up the huge country?

Notre Dame replied first with a lovely letter of admission telling me how privileged I was to have been offered admission. To reserve my spot I'd have to fork over a $100 deposit in two weeks. Berkeley had sent me housing forms but no acceptance letter. Wintry Cornell rejected me (thank you, God!), and I hadn't heard back from Texas or Miami. Panic began to set in and I sent in the $100 to Notre Dame to confirm my spot.

My trip to Mr. Desai, of Desai's Travel Mart ended in a rude surprise. In clear terms, Mr. Desai said it would be cheaper for me to get to South Bend via Chicago, and not through Miami. What! I knew from my geography that America's Midwest was a hardened land of bitter winters and hot summers. Growing wheat and ice fishing were the most important sports there. What had I done to deserve this gulag? But illogic prevailed and I calmed myself. If it got too cold in South Bend I might transfer to someplace warm after my freshman year.

Berkeley never responded with any finality, and so I decided to go to Notre Dame with optimism. Aleem got a full-scholarship to Harvard because he was, after all, our Golden boy. We weren't going to be kids any longer. Ladka, our chunky fun-filled friend got a spot at Middesborough University in the U.K.

Self important as a troop of mild-mannered monkeys, we spent the next few months sampling life. Ladka, with his massive sexual appetite, was making it with a girl whose virtues he was supposed to protect. (Ladka had promised a friend of his that he would keep his girlfriend safe from marauders while his friend left the country to study a year earlier). I was madly in love with my girl, Shemin, who continued to treat me like an unwanted rash. But she had agreed to be mine -- I had sealed that deal with a kiss, hadn't I?

Aleem, with no studying to do, came alive wanting to take chances with life, including letting his hair grow and sleeping with a woman for the first time. The three of us went on a wild trip to the coast, staying at a cheap beach house, eating meals out of tin cans, and trying to score with the middle aged German female tourists looking for African fun and sun. We weren't successful because we were too chicken to even say hello to white girls who spoke English in gruff accents. With little cash and a strong libido, Ladka's only alternative was to seduce a professional lady by selling or exchanging bits of jewelry that he wore – a lion's claw encased in a bit of gold and a ring made of malachite stone. Ladka made the woman laugh and feel special, and not like a disposable whore. She fell in love with Ladka who used this advantage to extract free daily sex. On quiet nights, we sang Hindi film songs, not caring how we sounded. The romantic moon shimmering in the warm water and the light monsoon winds exchanging whispers with the coconut palms showed us a slice of paradise. But we were young, eager for more adventure and ready to leave home.